Fun for Girls

Buster Books

Written by Ellen Bailey

Illustrated by Karen Donnelly, Lisa Jackson,
Ann Kronheimer and Nellie Ryan

Edited by Hannah Cohen, Elizabeth Scoggins
Jen Wainwright and Sophie Schrey

Designed by Zoe Quayle and Barbara Ward

Produced by Joanne Rooke

Cover from an original design and illustrations by Nikalas Catlow

First published in Great Britain in 2012 by Buster Books,
an imprint of Michael O'Mara Books Limited,
9 Lion Yard, Tremadoc Road, London SW4 7NQ

Fun For Girls contains material previously published under the titles *The Girls' Holiday Book,*
The Girls' Summer Book, The Girls' Rainy Day Book and *The Girls' Christmas Book.*

A CIP catalogue record for this book is available from the British Library.

ISBN: 978-1-78055-079-4

2 4 6 8 10 9 7 5 3 1

www.busterbooks.co.uk

This book was printed in January 2012
at Shenzhen Wing King Tong Paper Products Co. Ltd., Shenzhen, Guangdong, China.

WELCOME
TO A WORLD OF FUN

The following pages are bursting with fun things for you and your friends to make and do.

Come rain or shine, whether you're inside, outside, on the move or at home, this book will banish boredom for ever.

From puzzle challenges and great games to play, to gorgeous doodles to do and much, much more, you'll find something to enjoy whatever your mood.

All the answers are at the back of the book, but try not to peep until you have finished! So what are you waiting for? It's time to have fun, girls!

 # CONTENTS

ACTIVITIES

STORIES AND FACTS

DOODLES TO DO

ALL THE ANSWERS

ALL THE FUN OF THE FAIR

Roll up, roll up! Turn your living room into a fairground with these fun fête games, then invite your friends to come and play.

ROLL UP FOR THE RAFFLE

1. Find three items that you don't mind giving up as prizes for your raffle, such as a teddy bear, a chocolate bar and a funky headband.

2. Write the numbers '103', '107' and '115' on a piece of paper and cut them out. Use sticky tape to stick them to your prizes.

3. Fold a piece of A4 paper in half four times, then unfold it so that you can see the rectangular fold lines. Starting at 100, write a number in each of the rectangles, as shown until you reach 115. Cut along the fold lines and fold each rectangle in half. Place all the folded pieces of paper into a bowl.

100	101	102	103
104	105	106	107
108	109	110	111
112	113	114	115

4. To enter the raffle, each player must choose a piece of paper from the bowl. If the number matches one of the numbers stuck to a prize, the player wins that prize.

BEST ANIMAL IN SHOW

Ask your guests to bring their best animal cuddly toy to the fair, and explain why their toy is the best, including any special tricks they can perform. Each guest has to give each (animal) marks out of ten for appearance, special features and lovability. Whichever animal has scored the most points wins 'best in show'.

SPLAT THE RAT!

1. Make a 'rat' by cutting the feet off an old pair of nylon tights and stuffing one foot inside the other. Tie up at the top with string. Use felt-tip pens to draw eyes, nose and whiskers on to the stuffed part.

Make sure your rat is small enough to easily slide through a cardboard tube from inside a roll of wrapping paper.

2. Use sticky tape to attach the cardboard tube to a large piece of card.

3. Use felt-tip pens to write 'Splat The Rat' on to the card, then use lots of sticky tack to fix the card to the wall. The bottom of the tube should be just below your knee.

4. Each player must be given a kitchen roll tube to use as a bat. Drop the rat through long the tube for the player to try to hit the rat with the bat before it reaches the floor.

BOWLING SOCK BALLS

1. Line up a collection of seven clean empty yogurt pots upside down on the floor. Write a number from one to seven on a piece of paper and cut out each number. Pop a number randomly under each yogurt pot.

2. Place a piece of A4 paper on the floor about two metres away from the pots. Roll up a pair of socks into a ball.

3. Players must then take it in turns to roll the sock-ball across the floor to knock over as many yogurt pots as possible. Count up the points from inside each yogurt pot the player knocked over and write down their score. The person with the most points is the winner.

IT'S CAKE O'CLOCK!

Sunny summer days are the best time to throw an afternoon tea party. Read on to learn how to throw the perfect party.

CUTE CUPCAKES

Cute cupcakes are great tea-party food. Here's how to bake up a batch:

You will need:

For the cakes: • 2 eggs • 100 g caster sugar • 100 g self-raising flour • 100 g butter • 18 to 20 cupcake cases. **For the icing:** • 100 g icing sugar • 50 g butter • glacé cherries, chocolate buttons, sprinkles etc.

1. Turn the oven on to Gas mark 4/ 180 °C.

2. Place the cake ingredients into a large mixing bowl and stir with a wooden spoon until you have a smooth mixture.

3. Arrange your cupcake cases over

two bun tins – this mixture makes 18 to 20 cupcakes. Put two teaspoons of mixture into each case.

4. Ask an adult to bake the cakes in the oven for 10 to 15 minutes, or until they are golden brown on top.

5. Ask an adult to help you take the cakes out of the oven and place them on a wire rack to cool.

6. Put the icing sugar and butter into a bowl and stir until smooth.

7. Use a knife to spread the icing on the top of each cupcake. Decorate with cherries, chocolate buttons or whatever you like!

CAKE STAND PERFECTION

To add a touch of elegant sophistication to your tea party, why not make a cake stand to present your cute cupcakes on? Here's how:

You will need:

• 3 party cups (paper or plastic) • a sharp pencil • a blob of modelling clay • 3 m of gift ribbon • scissors • 2 small party plates • 1 paper party plate • sticky tape.

1. Position a cup on top of the modelling clay. Push the tip of the pencil through the middle of the cup base into the clay to make a small hole.

2. Do the same to the other two cups and the three plates.

3. Cut the ribbon into two equal lengths.

4. Holding the ends together, thread them through the hole in one cup, as shown below.

5. Thread the ribbons through the top of the small plate and then through the bottom of the second cup.

6. Now, thread the ribbons through the top of the other small plate and then through the bottom of the last cup.

7. Thread both the ribbon ends through the top of the large plate and secure the ends to the bottom of the final plate with sticky tape, as shown below.

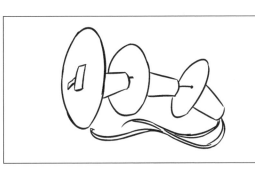

8. Hold the ends of the ribbon on to the first cup in one hand and sit the cake stand down on its base with the other hand. Carefully, tie the ribbon ends in a knot and finish with a bow.

9. Arrange the cupcakes on the cake stand.

Now all you need to do is plan the perfect tea party. Turn to page 110 to find out how.

PLAY THE CHESHIRE CAT

The Cheshire Cat is known for his mischievous grin, and getting people to smile is the aim of this game! Can you keep a straight face? Here's how to play:

1. A group of people sit in a circle with one person in the middle.

2. The person in the middle is the Cheshire Cat. Her job is to walk around on her hands and knees, purring and behaving like a cat in order to make the other players smile.

3. The Cheshire Cat should go up to each of the players in turn and say in a cat-like voice, 'Smile if you love me.'

The player must then respond, 'I do love you, Kitty, but I just can't smile.'

4. If any of the players smile at any point, whether she is talking to the Cheshire Cat or not, she becomes the Cat and must swap places with the person in the middle of the circle.

5. If none of the players smile, then the person in the middle continues going around asking everyone until she manages to get someone to smile.

FREAKY FOOD

People around the world have different ideas about what makes a tasty treat.

Can you guess which of the strange snacks below is eaten in which country?
Draw lines to match them up, and check your answers on page 184.
The first one has been done for you.

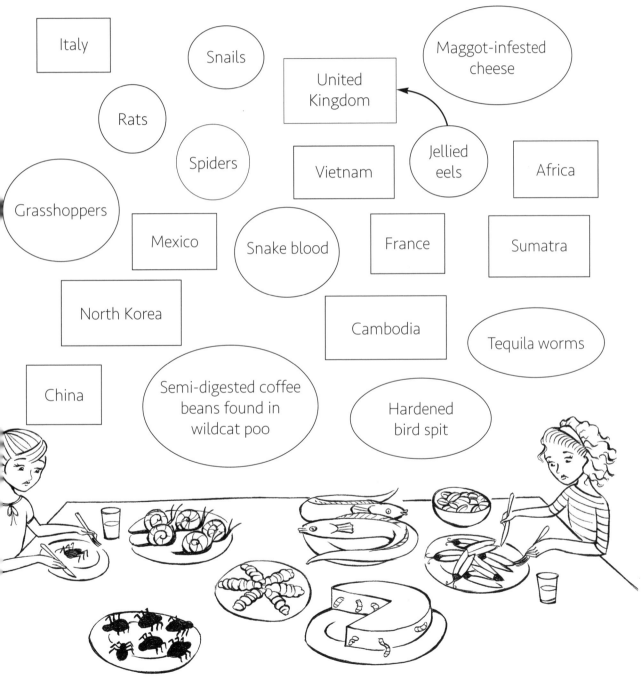

Italy

Snails

United Kingdom

Maggot-infested cheese

Rats

Spiders

Vietnam

Jellied eels

Africa

Grasshoppers

Mexico

Snake blood

France

Sumatra

North Korea

Cambodia

Tequila worms

China

Semi-digested coffee beans found in wildcat poo

Hardened bird spit

SHOP 'TIL YOU DROP

Complete the puzzles and turn to page 184 to check your answers.

You have 300 pence (p) in your purse. If you were going to use all of your money to buy one type of sweet, how many of each type could you buy?

Cola Bottles 17p

Bonbons 50p

Humbugs 10p

Toffees 20p

Lollipops 33p

Liquorice 60p

Candy Canes 85p

Sugar Mice 25p

Sherbet Lemons 45p

Can you find the sunglasses that match the ones pictured in the magazine above?

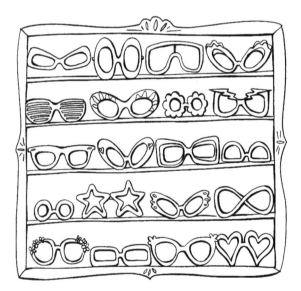

Can you spot 11 differences between the two window displays on the opposite page?

Decorate the lollipops and draw your own.

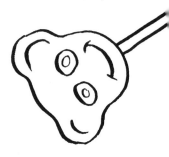

BORED ON BOARD?

Next time you are on a long journey,
try out these travel games and time will fly . . .

IN MY SUITCASE I HAVE PACKED ...

The first player says, 'In my suitcase I have packed ...', then names an item beginning with A, such as, 'an Alarm clock'.

The second player then says, 'In my suitcase I have packed ...', and then says the previous item, and one of their own that begins with a B, for example, 'an Alarm clock and a Ball'.

The game continues until you have been through the whole alphabet, or until a player forgets one of the items.

CELEBRITY INTERVIEW

Take it in turns to pretend to be a famous person who is being interviewed for a radio programme. The other players must ask you questions and use your answers to guess who you are.

COLOURFUL CARS

Each player picks a colour. The winner is the first to see 30 cars of their chosen colour.

ODD OR EVEN

Each player chooses 'odd' or 'even'. On the count of three, all players raise their hands, each holding up as many fingers as they want.

Count up the total number of fingers raised to find out if it is an odd or an even number. Those who guessed correctly score a point.

FAMILY ACT

Take it in turns to act like one of your holiday companions. The first person to guess who you are pretending to be scores a point and gets to have the next go.

Warning: Make sure no one gets offended – these travel games are supposed to make your journey more fun, not more stressful!

PICTURE THIS!

Using the grid lines to help you, draw your own version of this picture in the bigger grid below, with pens or pencils.

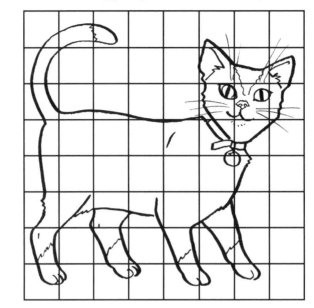

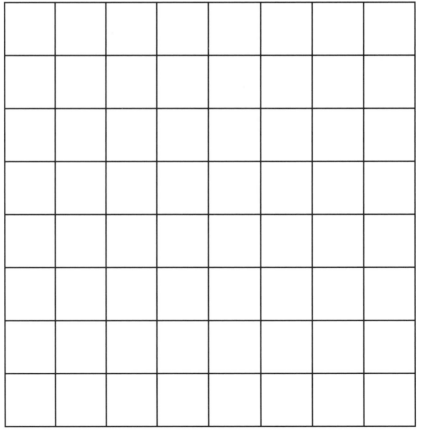

CRACK THOSE CODES

You find these bottles washed up on the beach. Three of them contain riddles written in secret codes, and the fourth contains cryptic clues that will help you crack the codes.

Match each clue to the correct bottle, decipher the messages, then figure out the answers to the riddles. Answers on page 184.

1

?I ma tahW
.erehwyna klaw
reven I tub ,kcab a
dna sgel ,smra
evah I

2

ySa ti dna uyo
lwil kerab ti.
thWa si ti?

3

Rfc kmpc wms
ryic md rfcqc
rfc kmpc wms
jcytc zcfglb.
Ufyr ypc rfcw?

4

Clue 1: Move each letter two letters forward in the alphabet

Clue 2: Back to front

Clue 3: Word scramble

PICNIC PERFECTION

Add some glamour when you plan a perfect picnic.

FABULOUS FLOWERS

To make these beautiful folded lotus flowers, all you'll need are some square napkins – it doesn't matter whether they are made of paper or fabric.

1. Open out the napkin and spread it flat. Fold each corner of the napkin into the centre, as shown below. You will now have a small square.

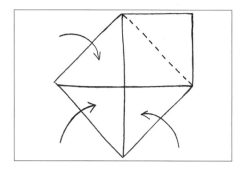

2. Fold each corner of the new square into the centre. You will now have an even smaller square.

3. Turn the napkin over, and again fold each corner into the centre.

4. Hold the centre of the napkin with one hand. Use your other hand to reach underneath the napkin and pick up one of the folded bottom corners.

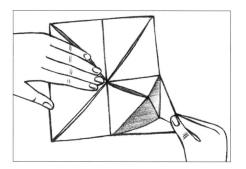

5. Pull the bottom corner up and out to create a petal. You'll need to push the top corner into the middle of the petal. Repeat for each corner.

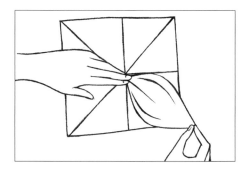

6. You will now have a flower shape. Keeping hold of its centre, reach underneath again and pick up one of the folded-in bottom corners from the inner layer. Pull it up and out to create a smaller petal.

7. Repeat for each of the four folded-in corners. You will now have a beautiful lotus flower.

PICNIC PUZZLE

The girls have made a list of some of the food at their picnic, but two of their items are wrong.

They think that there are:
5 cheese slices, 5 cupcakes, 4 croissants,
6 watermelon slices and 10 strawberries.
How many of each can you see?
Check your answers on page 185.

KITE CONFUSION

Six pieces from this jigsaw have got mixed up with some pieces from anothe
jigsaw. Can you find the six pieces needed to go in the gaps? Answer on page

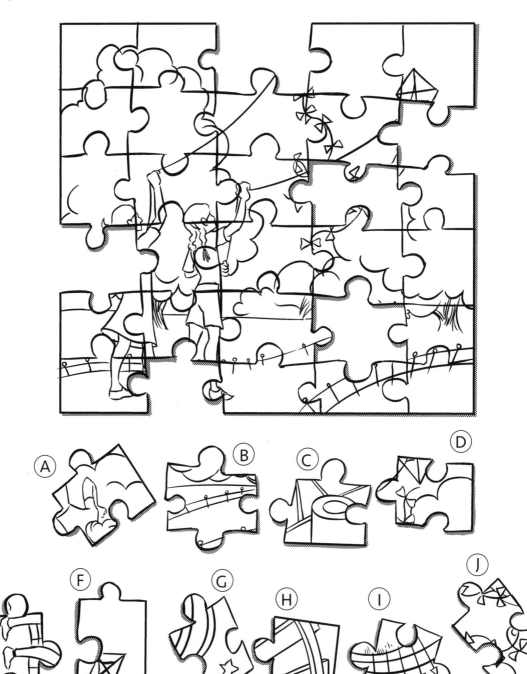

WRITE TO ME

Fill in your details on these cards. Cut them out and give them
to your friends, so you never lose touch.

Name: ....

Address: ....

....

Email: ....

Name: ....

Address: ....

....

Email: ....

Name: ....

Address: ....

....

Email: ....

Name: ....

Address: ....

....

Email: ....

Name: ....

Address: ....

....

Email: ....

Name: ....

Address: ....

....

Email: ....

Colour in each card
before you give it away.

AMAZING ANIMAL FACTS

One of these amazing animal facts is false – can you spot which one?
All will be revealed on page 185!

1. TASTY FEET?

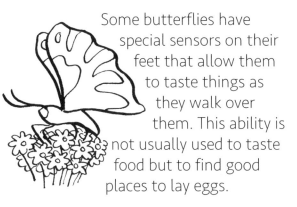

Some butterflies have special sensors on their feet that allow them to taste things as they walk over them. This ability is not usually used to taste food but to find good places to lay eggs.

2. SEE-THROUGH OR SO UNTRUE?

Some scientists believe that polar bears have transparent fur that only looks white because it reflects light.

3. POINTY BUT POSSIBLE?

Rhino horns are made from the same substance as human fingernails.

4. HOW 'EGGS'-ELLENT?

Hummingbirds lay the smallest eggs of any bird, as tiny as 7 mm long!

5. STRANGE SNACK?

There is a type of Asian moth that has evolved to feed on the tears of buffaloes.

6. ELE-FANTASTICAL?

Elephant pregnancies last for nine months, just like human pregnancies.

IT'S A BIRDIE!

This little bird makes such a cute present that
you might want to give it to yourself!

You will need:

• a pencil • a piece of paper • a sharp pair of scissors • a piece of fabric about the
size of this page (try to choose a fabric that doesn't fray easily, such as felt)
• pins • a needle and thread • 2 buttons • a pair of old socks.

What to do:

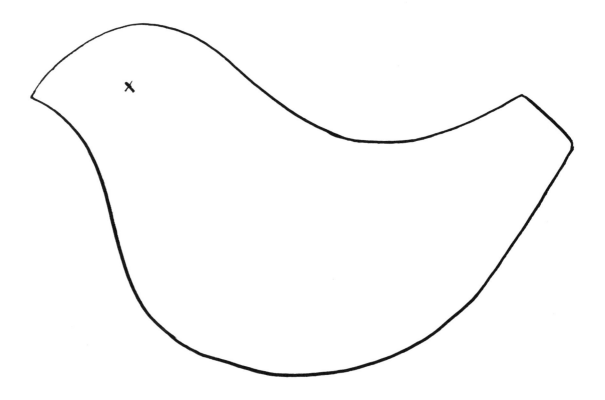

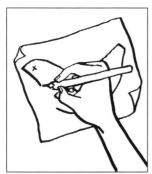

1. Trace over the picture of a bird, above, and cut it out. This is your template.

2. Fold the large piece of fabric in

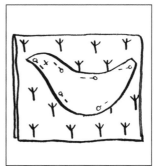

half with the printed side on the outside, if patterned.

3. Pin the paper bird on to the fabric, as shown here.

4. Carefully cut around the edge of the paper bird so that you end up with two matching fabric birds. Unpin the template.

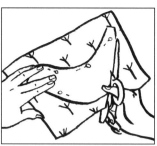

5. It's now time to sew some button eyes on to the fabric birds. Take a piece of thread the length of your arm and thread the needle. Pull the thread halfway through, then tie the ends in a double knot.

6. Place one of the buttons on the printed side of one of the fabric birds where its eye would be (marked with an X opposite).

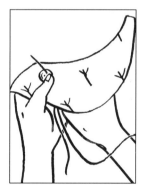

7. From below, push the needle up through the fabric and through one of the holes in the button. Pull it all the way through until the knot hits the fabric.

8. Push the needle down into the next hole and continue passing the needle up and down through the fabric and buttonholes until the button is secure.

9. Finish with the needle on the non-printed side of the fabric and secure it with a double knot. Trim the thread.

10. Sew the second button on to the other bird-shaped piece of fabric in the same way.

11. Pin the two bird-shaped pieces of fabric together so the printed-sides face outwards.

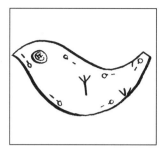

12. Thread the needle with another piece of thread about the length of your arm. Push the needle through the fabric about ½ cm from the edge.

13. Bring the needle back up through the fabric about 2 mm to the right of the first hole. Make several stitches on this spot to secure the thread.

14. Push the needle up and down through the fabric, making stitches that are 2 mm long.

15. Continue sewing around the bird until just a 2 cm hole is left.

16. Cut the socks into pieces, then push the pieces through the hole to stuff the bird.

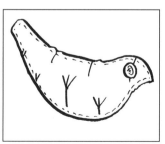

17. Sew the hole closed, then tie the end of the thread in a knot and cut off the excess.

Top Tip. Why not add a loop of ribbon, so that you can hang your birdie up?

WACKY WINDOW WELLIES

Brighten up your windowsill with these wacky Wellington-boot plant pots.

You will need:

• acrylic paints (or a selection of nail varnishes in different shades will do) • paintbrushes • a pair of old wellies • a metal corkscrew • some soil and gravel from the garden or local garden centre • a selection of seeds or plants.

1. Paint a design of your choice directly on to both boots. (Always rinse out your brushes with water when you have finished painting.)

2. Ask an adult to pierce a small hole through the sole of each boot, using a corkscrew. This hole allows excess water to drain out of your wellies.

3. Pour a cup of gravel into each boot and then fill up to the top with soil.

4. Bury some seeds just under the surface of the soil and pour some water over it. Place the boots on a small plate to catch any excess water, then pop on a sunny windowsill.

5. Water your wellies once a week, or if it's really hot, every other day.

WHAT SHALL YOUR GARDEN GROW?

Here are some ideas to get you started:

• Herbs and edible plants: cress, mustard or mint
• Pretty flowers: sunflowers, marigolds or pansies
• Fragrant flowers: lavender or sweet peas.

Top Tip. Plant ready-grown flowers rather than seeds for instantly pretty pots.

HOLIDAY STYLE QUIZ

Everyone looks forward to different things about going on holiday.
Take this quiz and find out what kind of holiday-maker you are.
Find out what your answers mean on the next page.

1. If you could take only one item on holiday with you, what would it be?

    A. Magazines

    B. Camera

    C. Sunglasses

    D. Beach ball

4. Which type of shoes do you spend most of your holiday wearing?

    A. Flip-flops

    B. Sandals

    C. High heels

    D. Trainers

2. Which item of clothing would you be most annoyed to forget?

    A. Sarong

    B. Favourite T-shirt

    C. Expensive new skirt

    D. Swimming costume

5. What is your favourite holiday drink?

    A. Milkshake

    B. Bottled water

    C. Fruit smoothie

    D. Energy drink

3. What is the first thing you do when you arrive at your destination?

    A. Get an ice cream

    B. Flick through a guidebook

    C. Hit the local shops

    D. Go swimming

6. How will you spend the last day of your holiday?

    A. Relaxing on a sun lounger

    B. Dashing round all the sights you haven't seen yet

    C. At the theatre

    D. Playing football with a new group of friends

WHAT YOUR ANSWERS MEAN

Count up how many times you chose each letter and then look at the results below to find out what your answers say about you. If you got an even mix of letters, then you're a girl who likes to try a bit of everything on holiday.

MOSTLY A: LAID-BACK LADY

When you're on holiday, your aim is to kick back and relax. You love lounging by the pool, indulging in long, lazy lunches, and flicking through magazines.

A week or two of this will leave you feeling totally chilled, but make sure you don't miss out on the fun because you've fallen asleep!

MOSTLY C: CITY STAR

You're a sophisticated girl who enjoys visiting new cities and getting to grips with the culture. You always look super-stylish, and love shopping and dining in posh restaurants.

Don't forget that even the most glamorous of girls need some down time, so make sure you leave time to pull on some comfy clothes and unwind.

MOSTLY B: SASSY SIGHTSEER

You're never seen without your camera, and love visiting famous landmarks. The more you can find out about your destination before you go, the more you'll get out of it. So grab that guidebook and get investigating.

MOSTLY D: ACTIVE ADVENTURER

Always the first to suggest a game of beach volleyball or Frisbee, you're a sporty chick who loves to keep active.

Exercise is a great way to relax and have fun on holiday, and will help keep you fit and healthy, too.

THE STRANGE CASE OF THE ISLAND CAVE BEAST

'I made a new friend at the beach today,' announced Lily to her sister, Kate. 'I fell over in a rockpool and a girl called Cat got some ice for me to put on my knee. She lives here on the island and she won the 'Young Surfer Of The Year' award this summer.'

'Hey, there she is!' exclaimed Lily as they rounded a corner. Kate looked in the direction her sister was pointing, but all she saw was a flash of grey.

'What on earth was that?' cried Lily, her heart pounding in her chest. Cat had disappeared and in her place was what looked like a huge animal that scampered off down the hill. 'Oh no!' exclaimed Kate. 'You don't think that was the Cave Beast do you?'

'I thought that was just something written in the guidebook to scare us,' said Kate, her voice shaking as she spoke. According to island legend, the Cave Beast was a fearsome creature that lived in an underground cave, but no one knew if it was real or not. 'It certainly did look like some kind of beast … and here's some grey fur caught on the wall.'

Lily felt a lump form in her throat. 'We've got to find her!' she exclaimed. 'I can see some more fur caught over there. Quick, they went this way.' The girls ran down the hill and stopped at the entrance to a cave. Lily was standing frozen looking into the entrance of the cave. Just inside was the red towel that Cat had been carrying earlier that day.

'We have to save her!' Lily grabbed hold of Kate's hand and pulled her into the cave. There was a long, dark tunnel ahead. As they approached the end, bright daylight momentarily blinded the girls, and their ears rang with the sound of children's voices. They were bewildered and frightened, but as their vision returned to normal they hugged each other in delight. 'It's a theme park!' exclaimed Kate.

'And there's Cat,' cried Lily. She rushed towards her. 'Cat!' she called. 'We saw you disappear with a giant animal and we thought you'd been captured by the Cave Beast!'

Cat laughed. 'This is the Island Theme Park, and that was just my friend Daniel. Here he is now.' Lily and Kate couldn't stop giggling as they were introduced to Daniel, who was dressed in a grey, furry animal suit.

'I can get you in for free,' Daniel offered. 'There's a Cave Beast ride I think you might enjoy!'

GO FISH!

Go Fish! is a card game for two to five players – perfect for a rainy day when you and your friends can't go out.

HOW TO PLAY

1. All you need is a deck of ordinary playing cards. Start by dealing seven cards to each player.

2. Spread out the remaining cards, face down, on the floor or a table. This is your 'pond'. Each card is a 'fish'.

3. The aim of the game is to catch as many full sets of four fish as you can – for example, four twos, four eights, four kings and so on. The player to the left of the dealer goes first and asks one of the other players if they have any of the fish they are looking for:

'Katie, do you have any threes?'

4. If Katie has any of the requested cards, she must hand them over. If she doesn't have any, she tells the player to 'Go fish!' That player must then take a card from the pond.

5. Continue playing around the circle to the left, following steps **3** and **4**. When a player collects four fish of the same value, she places them face up in front of her on the floor or table.

6. If a player uses up all her cards on a turn, she fishes a card from the pond and play passes to the next player.

7. The game ends when all the cards have been used, and all the sets of four fish have been completed. Whoever has made the most full sets wins.

HOT CHOCOLATE HEAVEN

When it's dark outside, and there's a chill in the air, there's nothing more cheering than a warming mug of hot chocolate.

You will need:

• 400 g caster sugar • 350 g cocoa powder
• enough milk to fill a mug • 10 miniature marshmallows.

What you do:

1. Mix the sugar and cocoa powder in a large mixing bowl using a whisk.

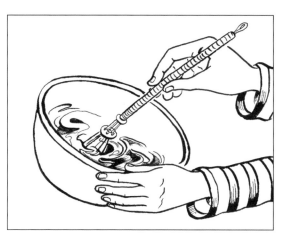

2. Place two heaped tablespoons of the mixture into a mug.

3. Pour the milk into a saucepan, and heat it on the stove until it's just starting to boil. Ask an adult to help you with this.

4. Turn off the heat, and carefully pour the hot milk into your mug. Ask an adult to help you.

5. Give the hot chocolate a good stir until the mixture has dissolved.

6. Sprinkle marshmallows on top.

7. Place the remaining mix into a storage container, so you can whip up a delicious cup of hot chocolate all through the Christmas holidays.

Festive Tip:

At Christmas time, instead of a spoon, why not use a candy cane to stir your hot chocolate?

It's sure to add a minty zing to your drink.

COOL SCIENCE

Turn your house into a laboratory with these exciting experiments.

HOW TO BRING A PAPER FISH TO LIFE

'Surface tension' is a property of all liquids. It is a bit like a layer of skin on top of the liquid. It is the reason that water collects in droplets and why small insects can walk on the surface of lakes and rivers. Carry out this science experiment to see the effects of surface tension in action.

Start by cutting out some fish from paper – trace the template of the fish opposite to make each one. Next, fill a washing-up bowl with water and place the paper fish flat on the surface.

Take a bottle of washing-up liquid and squeeze a small drop behind the tail of each fish. The soap will break the surface tension of the water, causing the fish to swim away at speed.

HOW TO MAKE A RAINBOW

Sunlight is made up of all the colours of the rainbow, and when it passes through water it splits up into light waves of different lengths, which we see as different colours. You can catch these light waves by standing a mirror in a saucer of water, on a table in front of a window.

Wait for a day when the sun is streaming through your windows for this experiment. Move the mirror around until the light passes through the water and bounces off the mirror, making a rainbow appear on the wall.

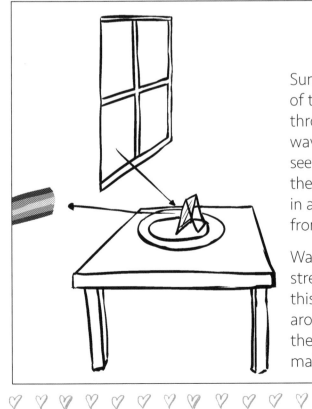

HOW TO MAKE A RAISIN DANCE

Prepare this experiment by filling a glass with water, and another glass with lemonade. Ask a friend what they think will happen when you drop a few raisins into the glass of water. She will probably guess correctly that the raisins will fall to the bottom. This is because objects sink when they are more dense than the liquid they're in.

Now ask your friend what they think will happen when you drop a few raisins into the lemonade. She will probably guess that the raisins will sink or float, but in fact they'll dance up and down in the lemonade for about an hour!

This is because of the bubbles of gas that make the lemonade fizzy. They attach themselves to sides of each raisin as it sinks to the bottom of the glass. When enough gas bubbles are attached to a raisin, it begins to float up to the surface again. When each raisin reaches the surface of the lemonade, the bubbles pop and cause the raisin to sink, until it becomes light enough to float again.

HOW TO MAKE YOUR EARS RING

The sound a guitar makes occurs because the vibration of the strings makes sound waves. You can create your own sound waves that will travel directly along a piece of string into your ears. All you need is a fork, a spoon and a long piece of string.

Tie the fork to the centre of the string, and tie one end of the string to your left index finger, and the other end of the string to your right index finger. Put one finger on each ear and let the fork dangle down.

Ask a friend to tap the fork with the spoon. The sound will travel up the string causing a loud ringing sound in your ears.

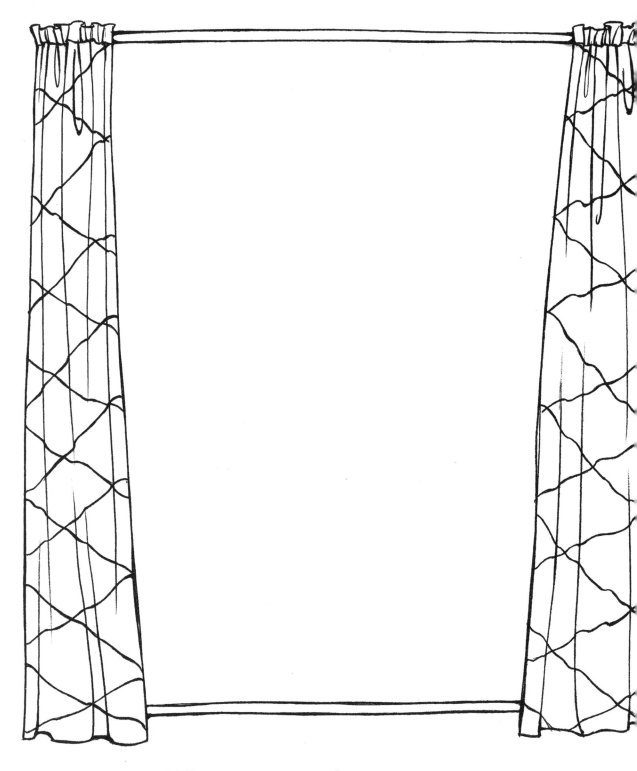

What can you see from your window?

FLOWER POWER

There are so many things to do on a rainy day that it can be hard to choose how to spend your time. Use some flower power to help you decide.

1. First, write an indoor activity that you enjoy in each of the flower petals below.

2. Count the number of letters in your first name, and add it to the number of letters in your surname.

3. Divide this number by two. If you end up with a half number, round it up. (For example, if you get 5.5, round it up to 6.)

4. Starting at the top petal, count round the flower petals until you reach your number, then shade in that petal.

5. Continue counting on the following unshaded petals, skipping any that are already shaded in. Every time you reach your number, shade in that petal.

6. When there is only one petal left, do that activity!

PUZZLE HOTEL

Complete the puzzles and turn to page 185 to find out the answers.

Can you spot seven differences between these two hotel rooms?

Look at these room keys.
Which two keys are exactly the same?

Can you find your way through the corridors to the rooftop restaurant?

Which bag belongs to which
family member?

HOW TO DRAW
A MERMAID

Create your own beautiful mermaid masterpiece by following these steps:

 **1.** Start near the top of a fresh piece of paper, and draw a half-oval shape for your mermaid's face. Add a long wavy line to this, coming from the top-right of her head and down to the left.

4. To begin your mermaid's arms, draw two long lines coming out to the left and two shorter lines coming out from beneath her hair.

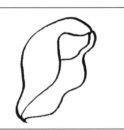

2. Build up your mermaid's hair by adding a long, curving line from the top-right of her head, down to the left, with a wide space between this and the first line. Then add a wavy line on the right-hand side of her face.

5. Copy the shape of the hands, as shown here, as closely as you can. Add the tail-shape by drawing two large S-shapes on the left, as shown above.

3. Fill out your mermaid's hair by drawing more wavy lines, as shown here. Then add her mouth, nose and eyes, trying to copy the shapes shown above as closely as you can.

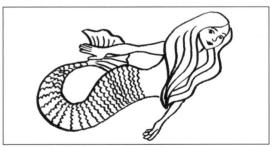

6. Now add a fan-shape to the end of the tail. Lastly, cover your mermaid's tail in small wiggly lines, like fish scales, to complete it. If you like, you can go over the lines of your finished drawing in black pen, before erasing the pencil lines. This will make it look really professional!

Design a crown and a necklace of flowers
for the Queen of Summer.

SPEAK UP

Wherever you are in the world, you'll meet holiday-makers from different countries. Become a true international jet-setter by learning to say, 'Hello, my name is …' and, 'Have a good holiday' in several different languages.

A guide to how to pronounce the words is given in *italics* below.

SPANISH

Hola, me llamo …
Ola, mee yammo …

¡Buenas vacaciones!
¡Bwenas vacatheeohnays!

ITALIAN

Buongiorno, mi chiamo …
Bwonjorno, mee kyamo …

Buona vacanza!
Bwona vacanza!

HINDUSTANI

Namaste, merās nām … ha
Nam-a-stay, merah nam … hi

Śubh yātrā!
Sub yah-trah !

FRENCH

Bonjour, je m'appelle …
Bonjhoor, jhuh mahpehl …

Bonnes vacances!
Bon vahkons!

GERMAN

Guten tag, ich heiße …
Gooten tahg, ick hi-ser …

Schöne Ferien!
Sherne ferry-en!

PORTUGUESE

Olá, meu nome é …
Ola, meeyoo nomeh eh …

Desejo-lhe umas boas férias!
Desayjo le oohmas bo-as fairy-as!

MANDARIN CHINESE

Nǐhǎo, wǒ jiào …
Neehaw, waw jow …

Yí lù píng ān!
Ee loo ping an!

TURKISH

Merhaba, benim adim …
Mehr-hah-bah, benim adim …

Güle güle!
Gew-leh, gew-leh!

RUSSIAN

Zdravstvujte, men'a zovut …
Zdra-stoy-chye, meen-ya zavoot …

Sčastlivogo puti!
Shess-lee-vovo pootey!

GARDEN GAMES

The girls are having plenty of fun in the sun in the garden scene below.
Why not join in the fun and have a go at completing these puzzles?
All the answers are on page 186.

Using only three straight lines, divide the garden scene below so that there
are only two girls in each section.

Can you spot the following animals and insects in the garden scene above?

• 11 birds • 7 butterflies • 5 cats • 7 ladybirds • 3 mice

WHAT'S YOUR SOCIAL STYLE?

When wet weather strikes, what do your choices say about you?
Try out this quiz to discover the true you!

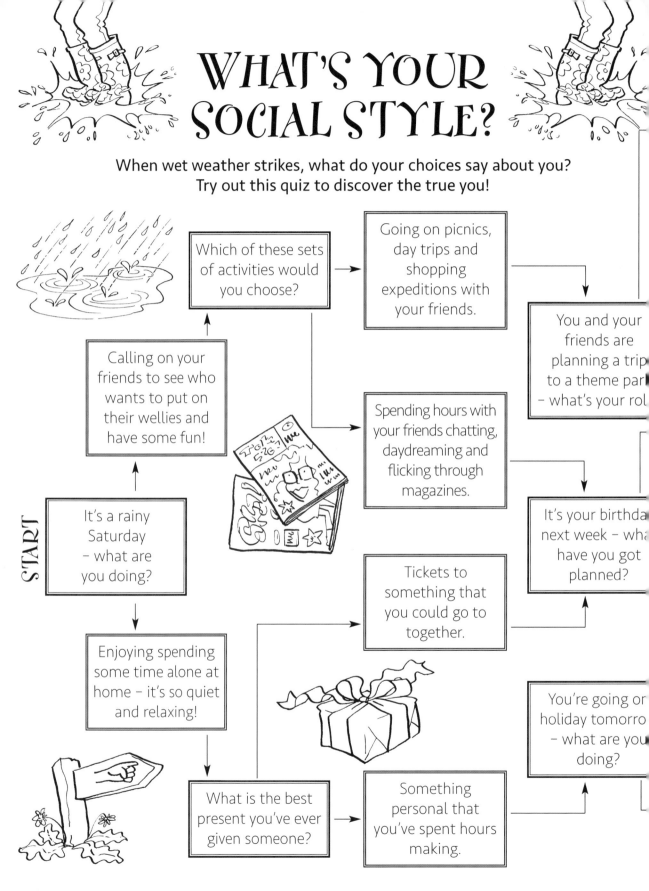

START

It's a rainy Saturday – what are you doing?

Calling on your friends to see who wants to put on their wellies and have some fun!

Which of these sets of activities would you choose?

Going on picnics, day trips and shopping expeditions with your friends.

Spending hours with your friends chatting, daydreaming and flicking through magazines.

You and your friends are planning a trip to a theme park – what's your role?

It's your birthday next week – what have you got planned?

Enjoying spending some time alone at home – it's so quiet and relaxing!

Tickets to something that you could go to together.

You're going on holiday tomorrow – what are you doing?

What is the best present you've ever given someone?

Something personal that you've spent hours making.

You're in charge of organizing everything and everyone.

→

LEADER OF THE PACK

You are full of energy and have a strong, passionate social style. Your friends love your ability to make things happen. You're ambitious and know your own mind.

You came up with the idea and got everyone excited about it – the details are up to someone else.

→

SOCIAL BUTTERFLY

You find it easy to make new friends and have a confident and relaxed social style. You're easy-going, creative and fun to be around.

You're having all your friends over for dinner and a sleepover.

→

LAID-BACK LADY

You are caring, kind and have an accepting and affectionate social style. Your friends know they can depend on you always to be there for them.

You've got lots of ideas and will make a spontaneous decision on the day.

→

Spending time with your best friend before you're separated – you can pack in the morning.

→

SOPHISTICATED SISTER

You're a deep thinker and have a self-reliant, independent social style. You are happy spending time on your own and have a small group of very close friends.

Double-checking that you've packed everything on your list.

→

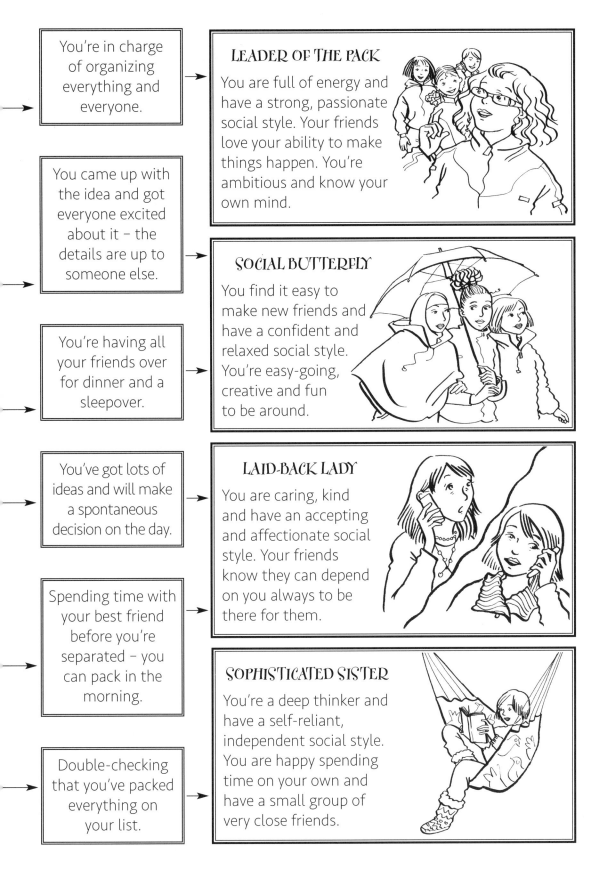

TOP-TO-TOE SUMMER BEAUTY

Whether you're heading off to the beach on your summer holidays or spending it at home, get ready to shine with these make-and-use summer beauty products.

HEALING HAIR WRAP

Sunshine, sea water and chlorine can all dry out your hair and leave it looking dull and straw-like, so try out this moisturizing conditioning treatment to restore shine.

First, warm a towel on a radiator or in a tumble-dryer. Next, wash your hair and slick a thick layer of conditioner on it before wrapping it in the hot towel. Leave for ten minutes. During this time use a hairdryer to warm your hair through the towel. Rinse, dry, and then show off your gorgeous silky locks.

HEAVENLY HONEY AND OATMEAL FACE MASK

Soothe sun-kissed skin with this cooling face mask. Mix one tablespoon of natural yogurt with one tablespoon of porridge oats and a few drops of honey.

Apply a thick layer to your face, avoiding the skin around your eyes, and leave for ten minutes. Rinse with warm water then apply a thick layer of moisturizer. Your face will now feel soothed and ready for another day in the sun.

SWEET SKIN BODY SCRUB

Relieve dry skin and remove dead skin cells with this delicious body scrub.

Pour two tablespoons of caster sugar into a bowl. Add the juice of half a lemon and four tablespoons of olive oil. Massage the mixture into your skin, then rinse off in a warm bath before bedtime. Pat your skin dry before getting into bed.

When you wake up in the morning, the remaining olive oil on your skin will have soaked in, making your skin feel sumptuously smooth.

GLITTER LIPGLOSS

You can dazzle on a summer's day simply by adding a flash of glitter. Find an old lipstick and scoop out the leftover colour into a bowl. Add some petroleum jelly and some craft glitter. Leave in the sunshine until it starts to melt.

Using a metal teaspoon, blend the mixture together. Scoop the mixture into the old lipstick case then place in the fridge to set. After one hour, dab some on your lips to complete your sparkly summer style.

REFRESHING LIME AND MINT FOOT SOAK

Walking around barefoot or in sandals can cause the skin on your feet to become rough. To soften up your feet, prepare a refreshing foot soak by putting ten mint leaves in a large bowl.

Chop a lime into quarters (ask an adult to help you with this), add to the bowl and use the back of a spoon to crush everything together.

Fill a clean washing-up bowl with warm water and add the limes and mint mixture. Soak your feet for 15 minutes until soothed and refreshed. Pat them dry with a clean towel and apply moisturizer. Your feet will now feel soft and smooth again.

DESERT-ISLAND DESSERTS

Bring some sunshine to your day with these delicious desert-island cupcakes. No one would mind being stranded on one of these islands!

You will need:

• 100 g butter, at room temperature • 100 g caster sugar
• 2 eggs • 100 g self-raising flour.

What you do:

1. Preheat the oven to 180 °C/350 °F/ Gas mark 4.

2. In a large bowl, beat the butter and sugar together using the back of a wooden spoon until the mixture is creamy and fluffy.

3. Crack one egg into the mix and stir it in thoroughly, then do the same with the other. Whisk until smooth.

4. Sift the flour into a separate bowl.

Warning: Always ask an adult to help you when you would like to use the oven.

5. Add the flour to the wet mixture a little at a time, using a metal spoon to gently 'fold' it in.

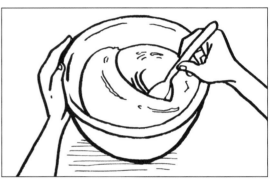

6. Place 12 cupcake cases in a bun tin and divide the cake mix evenly between them.

7. Bake for 20 minutes, or until lightly golden, and place on a wire rack to cool. Ask an adult to help you with this bit.

TRANSFORMING YOUR CUPCAKES INTO ISLANDS

You will need:

• 200 g butter, at room temperature • 400 g icing sugar • 4 tablespoons of milk
• blue food dye • chopped nuts • fish-shaped jelly sweets, if available
• chocolate fingers • green paper.

1. To make the topping, beat the butter with the back of a wooden spoon until it is soft, then gradually add the sugar. When you have beaten the sugar in, add the milk and mix thoroughly.

2. Ask an adult to check the cupcakes are cool and peel off the cases.

3. If the cakes have risen a lot, use a dinner knife to cut across the tops, so they are flat. Turn them over and spread topping over what is now the top of each cupcake to make into little islands.

4. Add several drops of blue food dye to the remaining topping and mix thoroughly. Use this to cover the sides of the cakes to make the ocean.

5. Next, sprinkle chopped nuts over your islands, before the topping dries, to make pebbly beaches.

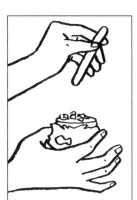

7. Gently push a chocolate finger into the middle of each desert island, so that they stand upright. These are the trunks of the palm trees.

8. Cut 36 leaves out of the green paper. Then use a dab of spare topping to stick each one to the top of the chocolate fingers (three per tree).

Enjoy your desert island dessert with friends!

6. Push your fish-shaped sweets into the sides of the cupcakes, as though they are swimming in the ocean.

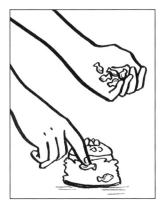

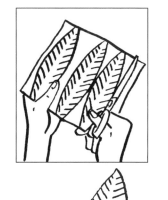

Warning: Make sure you leave out the nuts if you or your friends or family have a nut allergy.

Fill these photo frames with pictures of your friends and family.

48

SCARY STORY TIME

This is the perfect story to tell while sitting round a glowing campfire.

Read it through again and again until you know it by heart, then tell it to your friends on a dark, spooky night. Set the mood by shining a torch under your chin. When you get to the last sentence, whisper the words written in *italics*, then shout the word written in CAPITALS, and watch your friends jump out of their skins!

Did you hear the story that's been in the news about three girls from around here? They'd been out for the day and were heading home when they got caught in a storm. Without any warning, the wind began to howl and lightning flashed across the sky.

They ran up to a house and went to knock on the door, but saw that it was already open. It looked dark and scary inside, but there was no other shelter and they couldn't stay out in the storm, so they went in.

The house was deserted. It was dusty, cold and damp. Scared and wet, the girls huddled together in a corner. They could hear the rain hammering against the windows, and the wind was screeching through the house.

'What's that noise?' asked one of the girls.

'It's just the wind.'

'No, listen...'

Boom, shhhhhhh. Boom, shhhhhhh. Boom, shhhhhhh.

The sound was getting louder.

Boom, shhhhhhh. Boom, shhhhhhh. Boom, shhhhhhh.

Whatever the sound was, it was coming towards them. The girls put their arms round each other, their hearts beating fast in terror.

Boom, shhhhhhh. Boom, shhhhhhh. Boom, shhhhhhh.

There was something standing in the dark right next to them. They heard a voice:

'Don't worry, I'm only a little girl. But I've got a wooden LEG!'

PURR-FECT PETS

You're visiting a friend who has lots of pets. How many of each type of animal can you spot? Check your answers on page 186.

Dogs

Rabbits

Cats

Birds

Hamsters

Fish

Snakes

LUXURY LUGGAGE

Make sure your luggage is instantly recognizable and the most stylish in town with this fabulous oversized luggage tag.

1. Cut a large rectangle (that measures about half the size of this page) from a thick piece of card (an old cereal packet will do). Cut off the top and bottom corners of one side to make your tag shape. Use the point of a pencil to make a hole at one end of it – this will be the hole through which you can thread a ribbon to tie it to your bag.

2. Cut out enough paper to cover one side of your tag, and stick it on with glue. Write your name, postcode and telephone number on it. This means that if your luggage gets lost the person who finds it will be able to return it to you. You could decorate this side with felt-tip pens, and maybe even some glitter or sequins to make it really eye-catching.

3. During your holiday, collect paper souvenirs from your trip, such as ticket stubs, museum brochures, information pamphlets, postcards, sketches, maps, menus, interesting food packaging and stickers. Sort through the items you have collected and cut out pictures or words that look good and remind you of your holiday.

4. Cover the reverse side of your luggage tag with white PVA glue (dilute the glue with water if it's very thick). Stick the pictures on, then cover them with another thick layer of glue.

5. When the glue has dried and the surface of your tag looks shiny, thread a piece of brightly coloured ribbon or string through the hole and tie it on to the handle of your bag.

BUSY BEES

Busy Bees is a game for two players.
Be the first to form a connected path
of honey from one side of the
hive to the other.

To play, you will need a red pen and a
blue pen. Take it in turns to shade in any
hexagon on the board below.

Player **A** must try to create a linked
path from the top left to the
bottom right of the hive. Player **B**
must try to create a linked path
from the top right to the
bottom left of the hive.

SNEAKY BEES

You can use sneaky-bee
tactics and use your turn
to block your opponent.

Player A starts here

Player B starts here

Player B finishes here

Player A finishes here

RELAX TO THE MAX

Here's the perfect opportunity to wind down and de-stress. Spend some time looking after your mind and body with these relaxation techniques. Choose from the following, or make a day of it and do them all!

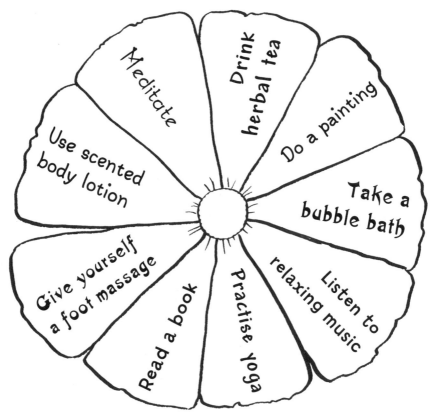

Meditate

Drink herbal tea

Do a painting

Use scented body lotion

Take a bubble bath

Give yourself a foot massage

Read a book

Practise yoga

Listen to relaxing music

MEDITATION STATION

Meditation is a great way to help you feel calmer and more relaxed. Here's how to get started:

1. Sit cross-legged on the floor.

2. Concentrate on your breathing and take ten long, deep breaths. When you breathe in, imagine peace and calm entering your body, and when you breathe out, imagine all the tension leaving your body.

3. Continue to breathe deeply and evenly, but now focus your mind on all the good things in your life. Think about the people you love and the things you enjoy doing. This will help you to feel calm, happy and full of energy.

4. Finish with five more long, deep breaths.

5. Write down any ideas or thoughts that came to you during your meditation in a notebook.

SIX-STEP YOGA

As well as making you feel more relaxed, yoga is a great way to stretch your muscles and to improve your flexibility. Try holding each pose in this series for a minute and see how you feel.

1. Lie flat on your back with your palms facing the ceiling.

2. Hug your knees to your chest.

3. Sit up and stretch your legs out in front of you. Place your hands on the floor at your sides. Gently bend your neck and tilt your head forwards towards your chest.

4. Stand up. Stretch your arms up above your head and press the palms of your hands together.

5. Raise one foot off the ground and rest it against the side of your other leg. Repeat with the other foot.

6. Lastly, shake your body out like this.

CINEMA RACERS

It's Friday afternoon and the school bell has just rung. Race your friends through the park to get to the cinema in time for the start of the film.

Place a coin for each player in the start box then take it in turns to spin the spinner (follow the instructions opposite to find out how) and move forward the number of spaces shown.

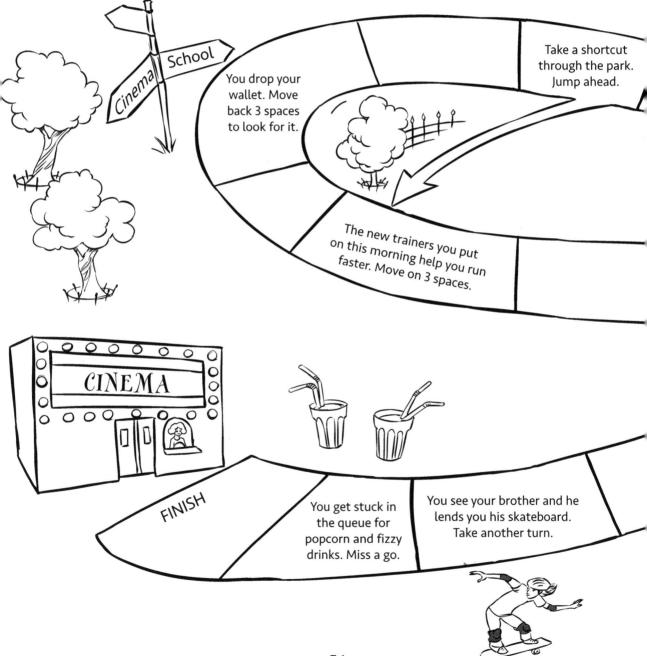

Cinema   School

You drop your wallet. Move back 3 spaces to look for it.

Take a shortcut through the park. Jump ahead.

The new trainers you put on this morning help you run faster. Move on 3 spaces.

CINEMA

FINISH

You get stuck in the queue for popcorn and fizzy drinks. Miss a go.

You see your brother and he lends you his skateboard. Take another turn.

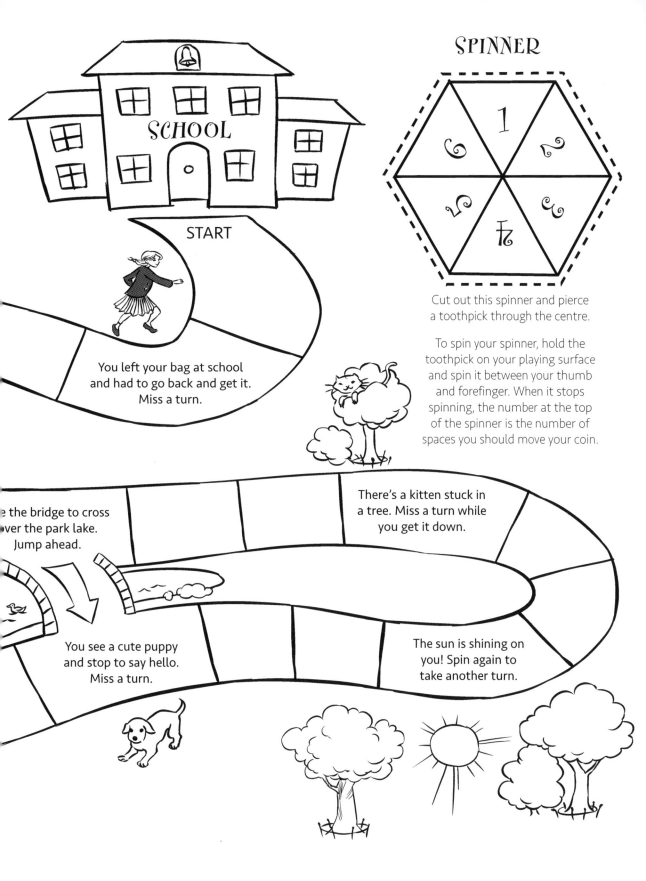

SCHOOL

SPINNER

START

1
2
3
4
5
6

Cut out this spinner and pierce a toothpick through the centre.

To spin your spinner, hold the toothpick on your playing surface and spin it between your thumb and forefinger. When it stops spinning, the number at the top of the spinner is the number of spaces you should move your coin.

You left your bag at school and had to go back and get it. Miss a turn.

e the bridge to cross ver the park lake. Jump ahead.

There's a kitten stuck in a tree. Miss a turn while you get it down.

You see a cute puppy and stop to say hello. Miss a turn.

The sun is shining on you! Spin again to take another turn.

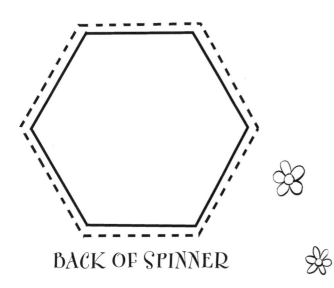

BACK OF SPINNER

Fill the page with flowers, butterflies, bees and ladybirds.

SURF'S UP!

Everybody's gone surfing. Grab your board and join
in with these surf activities.

POP-UP ON YOUR BOARD

Don't let a lack of waves to ride bother you. If you are a true surfer girl, you can
perfect a surfing technique called a 'pop-up' whether you're on the beach or in
your bedroom. Here's how:

1. Place a towel on the floor and fold it
lengthways.

2. Lie on your stomach along the towel,
and paddle your arms as though you're
swimming your board through the
water.

3. When you're ready to catch a wave,
place your palms flat on the towel
underneath your shoulders. Keeping
your body straight, use your arms to do
a full push-up, as shown below.

4. Pull your knees towards your
stomach, hop onto your feet, and stand
up with one foot in front of the other
on the 'board'. This is called a 'pop-up'.

The pop-up should be one swift,
smooth motion straight to a standing
position. So keep practising until you're
a super-confident surf chick.

BREAKFAST IN BED

What better way to celebrate the weekend than with a delicious breakfast in bed, served on a beautiful home-made tray?

You can make breakfast for yourself and take it back to bed, or treat your parents to a beautiful breakfast surprise.

A TRAY FOR YOUR TREATS

Follow the instructions below to find out how to make a pretty breakfast tray to present your tasty treats on.

You will need:

• an old wooden tray (check it's okay to use first) • a selection of old magazines • brightly coloured acrylic paints • paintbrushes • PVA glue.

1. Paint a thick layer of brightly coloured paint on both the inside and the outside surfaces of the tray. Leave the tray to dry completely.

2. Look through your magazines, and cut out any pictures that you think will look good on your tray – a selection of summery flowers is perfect.

3. Arrange the pictures on the middle of the tray and move them around until you are happy with how they look.

4. Stick your pictures on to the tray using PVA glue.

5. Using a large paintbrush, cover the whole of the tray with PVA glue. This will fix your pictures in place and give the tray a shiny, professional finish. Don't forget to cover the painted areas too.

6. Leave the tray to dry overnight before using it.

BREAKFAST PERFECTION

When you wake up in the morning, follow the steps below
to prepare a brilliant brekkie.

1. Pour a glass of your favourite fruit juice and add a couple of ice cubes.

2. Choose your favourite breakfast food to serve as the main dish. Cereals should be served already poured out into the bowl, with a small jug of milk by the side. Bread, toast or croissants should be served on a pretty plate with a small dish of butter or other spread, and perhaps some jam by the side.

3. Make a fruit salad by chopping lots of different types of fruit into bite-sized pieces. (Ask an adult to help you when chopping fruit with knives.) Mix the fruit together in a bowl with a cup of your favourite fruit juice – the acid in the juice will stop the fruit turning brown in the bowl.

4. Fold a napkin or a paper towel in half to form a triangle and place it in the corner of your home-made tray.

5. Present the rest of your breakfast neatly on the tray. Pop all the cutlery you will need on top of the napkin.

Top Tip. For an extra-special touch, fill a small vase with flowers and place it in the top right-hand corner of the tray.

DID YOU KNOW?

A 'fast' is a long period of time without eating – so 'breakfast' means breaking the fast you've been on since the night before.

WET WEATHER WISHES

When the weather outside is frightful, it's time to decide whether you'd rather splash around in puddles or curl up with a good book.

If it is raining outside, I am more likely to …

… be happy – I love the rain! ☐

… hope for a rainbow. ☐

… feel miserable. ☐

… have fun indoors. ☐

The last thing I want to do when it rains is …

… let it change my plans. ☐

… go outside. ☐

… get wet feet. ☐

… stay at home. ☐

The best thing to do if I am out in the rain is …

… splash in the puddles! ☐

… drink raindrops. ☐

… spin my umbrella. ☐

… have a water fight. ☐

When the weather is wet, I'd rather be …

… shopping with my friends. ☐

… playing in the park. ☐

… riding my bike. ☐

… reading in the sun. ☐

If it's raining, my parents are most likely to say …

… 'It's good for the plants.' ☐

… 'Do some homework.' ☐

… 'Help me around the house.' ☐

… 'Play outside anyway.' ☐

On a rainy day, the best thing to do indoors is …

… imagine I'm somewhere hot. ☐

… play with my brother or sister. ☐

… watch a DVD. ☐

… curl up with a good book. ☐

Decorate these girls' umbrellas.

HOLIDAY HIGHLIGHTS

When you next go on holiday, answer these questions at the end of your trip, so you'll remember it for ever.

Holiday Destination: ....

Dates – From: .... To: ....

Who went with you?

Describe the place where you were staying.

What was your favourite holiday activity?

What was the funniest thing that happened?

If you could re-live one day of your holiday, which would it be?

What was the most delicious thing you ate?

Was there anything that you did for
the first time during your holiday?

Did you make any new friends?
What are they like?

What was your favourite
holiday outfit?

What will you miss most now
you're back at home?

HOME SWEET HOME

School holidays are perfect for enjoying time at home. So pop your slippers on and settle down to these homey puzzles. All the answers are on page 186.

SUDO-COOK

Complete this sudoku grid, so that the four different kitchen items shown below – the oven glove, the spoon, the saucepan and the mixing bowl – appear only once in each column, each row, and in each of the four larger squares.

TIME FOR TEA

Can you match the teacups to their saucers below in time for tea?

BUNKBED MADNESS

Four sleepy girls want to go to bed. Can you find which bunk belongs to which girl?

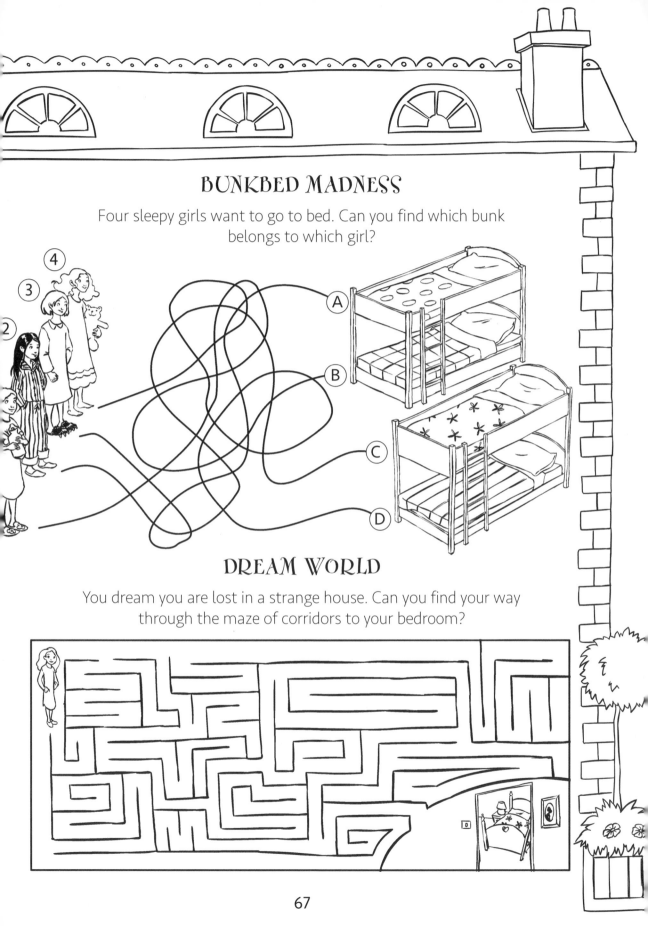

(A)
(B)
(C)
(D)

DREAM WORLD

You dream you are lost in a strange house. Can you find your way through the maze of corridors to your bedroom?

GIRL POWER!

Take inspiration from these incredible girls.

TSUNAMI HERO

While on holiday in Thailand in 2004, Tilly Smith, an 11-year-old from Surrey in England, noticed that the sea was strangely bubbly. Just two weeks before, her class had been learning about giant waves, known as tsunamis, and had watched a film about one that struck in Hawaii, in 1946. She knew these were danger signs.

Tilly said to her mum, 'Seriously, there is definitely going to be a tsunami.' Finally her mum started to listen, and the family took refuge with minutes to spare. That day, Tilly saved the lives of her family and over 100 other people. She received a special award for her quick thinking.

NO STOPPING HER

Born in 1990, surfer Bethany Hamilton, from Hawaii in the USA, could catch a wave by the time she was seven years old. By the age of 13, she had won lots of local surfing competitions and was on her way to becoming a professional.

One terrifying day, Bethany was in the sea with her best friend Alana when they were attacked by a tiger shark. The shark was over 4 metres (13 feet) long and it tore off Bethany's left arm. She lost more than 60% of her blood, but she survived.

Bethany refused to give up her surfing career and was back on her board just 26 days later. In 2005, she came first in the Explorer Women's division of the national championships!

These two girls took their right to an education into their own hands.

SCHOOL FOR ALL

Thandiwe Chama is from Lusaka, in Zambia. When her school was shut down because it had no teachers left, Thandiwe led 60 pupils in a march to find another place to learn. She was just eight years old, but Thandiwe was determined that they should receive an education.

The pupils were taken in by another school, but as there wasn't enough space, they were taught outside in the hot sun. Thandiwe persuaded a local official to pay for a new building.

Since then, Thandiwe has been fighting for a right to education for all children, no matter how poor they may be.

In 2007, she was awarded the International Children's Peace Prize.

PRIZE-WINNING CAMPAIGN

The 2008 winner of the International Children's Peace Prize was Mayra Avellar Neves from Brazil. Mayra grew up in a poor area of Rio de Janeiro – one of the most dangerous cities in the world. When she was 15 years old, the violence in the area where she lived became so bad that all the schools and hospitals closed down.

Bravely, Mayra organized a protest march to draw attention to the problems there. Hundreds of people took part, and, as a result, children were able to return to school. Mayra then organized another march to campaign for fairer treatment of people who live in slums.

HELLO, HANJIE!

Konnichiwa! (That's 'hello' in Japanese.) Hanjie is a brain-boggling Japanese puzzle that's perfect for *tsuyu* – the rainy season. See how quickly you can complete these challenges, then turn to page 187 for the answers.

Shade in squares in these puzzles to reveal the hidden images. The numbers at the end of each row and column reveal the number of shaded squares that appear together in that row or column, in order, from left to right or from the top down.

For example, the clue '1, 1' tells you that you need to shade in a single square, then leave a gap of at least one square before shading in another single square somewhere in that row.

Novice

Get started with this easy-peasy puzzle for beginners. Look at the numbers along the top of the grid – do you notice that one column should have all five squares filled? Start there, and you should soon find the spaces filling up!

	1	3	5	3	1
3					
5					
3					
1					
1					

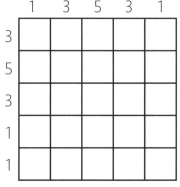

Expert

This one is slightly trickier, so some of the squares have been filled in for you. Remember, if there is more than one group of shaded squares in a row or column, there must be a gap of at least one square between them.

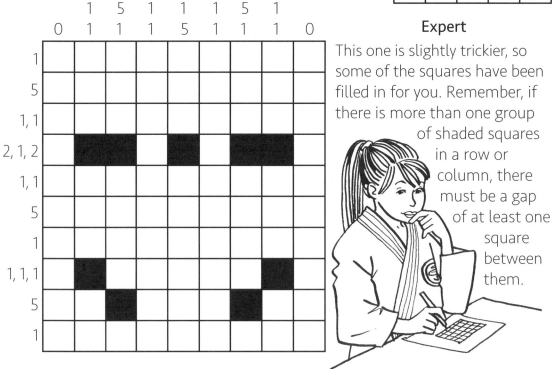

EAGLE EYES

Who'll be the first of your family or friends to spot each of the items below?

Write that person's initials in the box next to the item. The winner is the person who spots the most. You might be able to spot everything listed on a long car journey, or why not try playing the next time you go away?

WHAT CAN YOU SPOT?

1. Traffic lights		16. A bakery	
2. A train station		17. A white van	
3. Someone wearing red		18. A supermarket	
4. A dog		19. A taxi	
5. A police car		20. An aeroplane	
6. A hairdresser's shop		21. A book shop	
7. A bus stop		22. A museum	
8. A bridge		23. A washing line	
9. A lorry		24. A convertible car	
10. Someone taking photos		25. Someone using a phone	
11. Someone on roller skates		26. A restaurant	
12. A caravan		27. Someone wearing a uniform	
13. A baby		28. A cinema	
14. Flowers		29. A sweet shop	
15. A phone box		30. A fire engine	

PERSEPHONE'S PROBLEM

'Come on Artemis. Keep up!' shouted Persephone as she sat laughing in the sunny meadow. Just as Artemis threw herself down next to her friend, the ground next to them opened up and flames leapt up out of the hole. The girls screamed in terror as a man appeared in the flames.

'I am Hades,' he bellowed, 'God of the Underworld.' He grabbed Persephone's arm and pulled her through the flames into the hole in the ground. They had disappeared into the Underworld!

When Artemis told Persephone's mother, the goddess of harvests and farming, what had happened, the sun hid behind black clouds, the birds stopped singing and the leaves fell from the trees. 'Without Persephone, there can be no summer!' she cried. And sure enough, as weeks passed and Persephone could not be found, a winter frost covered the ground.

Persephone's mother visited Zeus, King of the Gods, and begged him to help her. 'Your daughter is in the Underworld,' replied Zeus. 'She can only return if no food has touched her lips since she has been there.'

Meanwhile, in the Underworld, Hades had fallen in love with Persephone. He presented her with a fruit called a pomegranate. Persephone had not seen the sun for many weeks, and the fruit reminded her of summer. She put six of the seeds into her mouth, and they were the most delicious things she had ever eaten.

Eventually, Zeus decided that Persephone could return to her mother. However, because she had eaten the six pomegranate seeds and had broken his rule, she would have to spend six months of every year living in the Underworld with Hades.

Artemis was overjoyed to see her friend when she came back and Persephone's mother was so happy that the ice melted and summer returned. But each year when Persephone had to go back to the Underworld, winter would once again descend.

PERSEPHONE'S PINK POMEGRANATE PUDDING

Pomegranate seeds look like beautiful pink jewels, and you can buy this delicious fruit in most supermarkets and greengrocers.

To make a pretty pink pomegranate pudding that'll bring the feeling of summer into your dining room, follow the steps below.

You will need: (this recipe serves 4)

- 1 ripe pomegranate • a large pot of plain yogurt
- 9 shortbread biscuits • some fresh mint leaves.

1. Place eight of your shortbread biscuits in a plastic food bag. Use the end of a rolling pin to bash them into small pieces.

2. Remove the biscuit crumbs from the plastic bag and divide them between four glass tumblers.

3. Cut the pomegranate into quarters and place in a large bowl of water.

4. Keeping the pomegranate below the surface of the water, use your fingers to remove all the seeds. The seeds will sink to the bottom and any white pith will float to the top.

5. Remove the pith from the top of the water with your hands, then use a sieve to drain the seeds.

6. Empty the yogurt into a mixing bowl and add the pomegranate seeds. Use a metal spoon to mix them together, and watch as the yogurt turns pink.

7. Spoon the pink yogurt mixture into each of the tumblers.

8. Crumble some of the extra shortbread biscuit on top of the pudding and decorate with a few fresh mint leaves. Serve with a spoon. Yum!

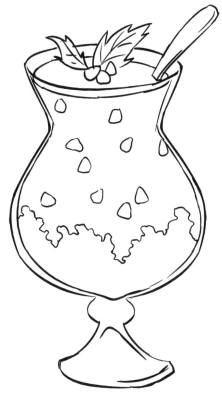

STAY COOL

When the temperature rises, keep your cool with these top tips.

HOT HEAD

If your head's cool the rest of your body will be too. To cool down, simply dip a headscarf in cold water then wring it out so that it's damp, but not dripping. Wrap it over your head and tie in a pretty bow at the base of your neck.

WATERMELONADE

This delicious watermelon lemonade is perfect for cooling yourself down on a hot day. Cut slices of watermelon, remove the peel and pick out the seeds. Blend in a food processor – ask an adult to help you with this.

Press the pulped watermelon through a strainer into a large jug. Add lemonade and mix together with a whisk. Garnish with slices of watermelon and a sprig of mint.

FRUITY CUBES

Fill an ice tray with water. Cut pieces of lemon and lime and place one in each cube. Carefully slide the tray into your freezer and leave for a couple of hours. Add to summer drinks for a cool citrus chill.

OCEAN SPRAY

Find an empty bottle with a spray function – hair products and suntan lotions often come in this kind of bottle. Thoroughly wash the bottle so that there's none of the old product left inside.

Fill the bottle with water and squirt a little of your favourite perfume into the bottle. Keep it in the fridge and use it to have a quick refreshing spray after being outdoors.

FAN-TASTIC

Draw a pretty pattern on a piece of A4 paper. Pleat the paper by folding every two centimetres, as shown below.

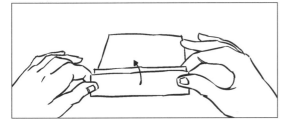

Take two lollipop sticks and glue one to each end of the paper so that the top of each stick is in line with the top of the paper. Tie a piece of ribbon around the bottom of the paper to create a handle.

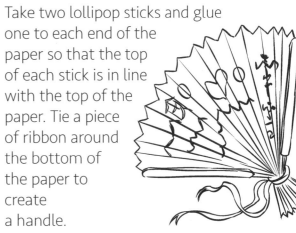

WATER COOLER

Keep bottles of drinking water in the freezer and take one with you when you're going out to play in the sunshine. The ice will gradually melt, giving you a supply of cool, refreshing water.

If you are hot when you go to bed at night, pop a bottle of frozen water in front of a fan. The chilled air will get pushed around the room and cool you down.

HOLIDAY BINGO

This is a great game that you can play anywhere – on a long journey, on a rainy day or at the beach.

Holiday Bingo is a game for three players. Find out how to play below, then cut out the boards and counters on the next page and you're ready for some bingo fun.

1. You are all going on holiday together, but one player has lost their suitcase and needs to borrow items from the other two. Choose which of you will be the 'suitcase' players and who will be the 'lost luggage' player.

2. Cut out the suitcase game boards and each of the counters. The two 'suitcase' players then choose either the suitcase and counters with the hearts, or the ones with the flowers. (See page 78.)

3. Without letting the 'lost luggage' player see, the two 'suitcase' players choose six of their counters and place them all face-up on their suitcase game boards.

4. The 'lost luggage' player then calls out in a random order the items from the list below that they would like to borrow.

5. Each time the 'lost luggage' player says the name of an item that one of the 'suitcase' players has on their game board, that player hands the matching counter to the 'lost luggage' player.
The winner is the first player to hand over all the items that are on their suitcase game board.

LIST OF ITEMS

1. Travel sweets	**7.** Sunglasses
2. T-shirt	**8.** Magazine
3. Towel	**9.** Day bag
4. Camera	**10.** Money
5. Toothpaste	**11.** Hat
6. Hairbrush	**12.** Travel pillow

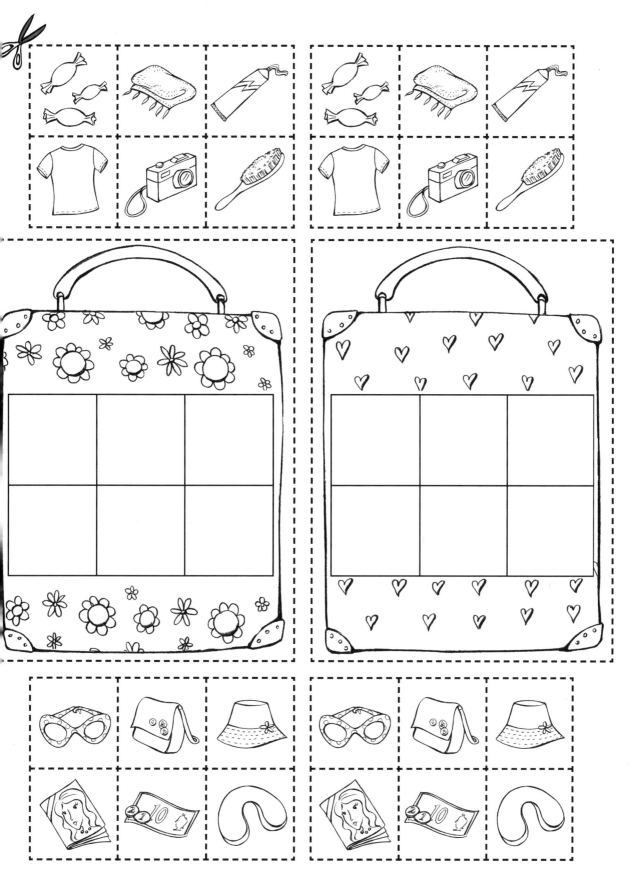

Draw the missing girls standing in front of these body-bending mirrors.

SLEEPOVER PUZZLER

The girls are having a sleepover, so grab a pen and test your skills in these chums' challenges! You'll find the answers on page 187. First, can you find your way through the maze to get to the sleepover on time? On the way, you need to pick up your friends Katie and Jessie.

Katie

SLEEPOVER
MYSTERY
MAZE

Jessie

DRESSING-GOWN DILEMMA

Can you work out which dressing gown belongs to which girl?

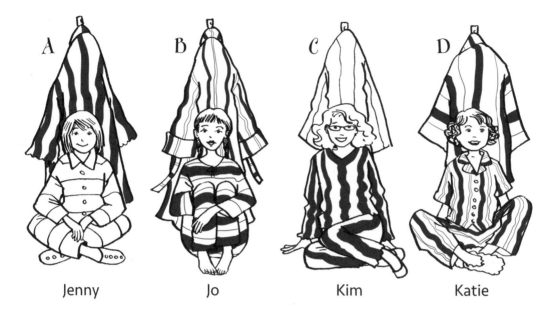

A   B   C   D

Jenny   Jo   Kim   Katie

SNACK TIME!

The girls are having pizza for their midnight feast. Two of them have chosen identical slices – can you spot which two are identical?

A   B   C

D   E   F

MIDDLE-NAME LOGIC

The girls are trying to guess each other's middle names. Can you give them a helping hand? Write the correct first name next to the middle names below, using the following clues:

1. Jenny's middle name starts with an S.

2. Jo's middle name has an L in it.

3. Kim's middle name is not the longest.

4. Katie's name is as long as Jenny's.

. . . . Isabelle

. . . . Coral

. . . . Sophie

. . . . Sarah

HOPPING ORIGAMI

Make an origami frog that really hops! You can then use it as a counter for the lily-pad game on the next page. All you need is a square of froggy green paper.

1. First, fold the piece of paper in half.

the two sides together so that they meet in the middle.

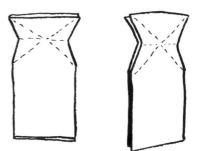

2. Fold the top-left corner down, so that the top of the paper lines up with the right-hand side. Then unfold it again.

The top of the paper will now fold down to form a triangle, like this:

3. Now fold the top-right corner down, so that the top of the paper lines up with the left-hand side. Then unfold it again.

6. Fold the bottom of the paper up so that the edge lines up with the bottom of the triangle.

4. Turn the paper over and fold down the top at the point where the diagonal creases meet, to make a horizontal crease, as shown here.

7. Fold the corners at the bottom of the triangle up to make the frog's front legs.

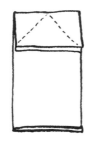 

5. Unfold the paper again and hold it by the edges of the horizontal line. Bring

8. Next, fold in the straight sides, so that they meet in the middle.

9. Fold the straight sides up, so that they reach the bottom of the frog's legs. Unfold them again, leaving a crease.

10. Reach under the flaps at the bottom with your thumbs, holding the middle in place with your fingers. Pull the flaps upwards and outwards into points, so that the lower edge comes up to reach the bottom of the frog's legs.

Note: If you would like to make frog counters to play Lily-Pad Hoppers (see pages 84-85), start with a square of paper measuring roughly 10 cm across. Use a different shade for each player.

11. Fold the points down, so that they meet at the bottom, as shown here.

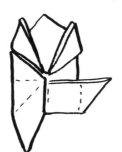 

12. Now fold these points out diagonally to make your frog's back legs.

13. Next, fold your frog in half across the middle, then fold the back legs back again in a zigzag, so that the frog's back legs will be underneath its body.

14. That's it! Turn your frog over. To make it hop, press and flick on its back. You can use your frog for a game of Lily-Pad Hoppers on the next page.

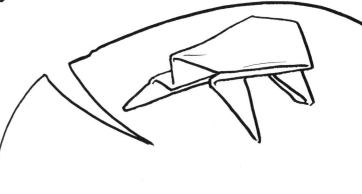

83

LILY-PAD HOPPERS

Race your friends across the pond and be the first to make it to the riverbank on the other side!

First, get each of your friends to make an origami frog as a counter (see pages 82 and 83). Alternatively, use a different coin each instead. Place the frogs at the start, then take turns to spin the spinner (follow the instructions opposite to get spinning) and move forward the number of spaces shown.

You stop to lo[ok at] some tadpol[es.] Miss a tur[n.]

Take a shortcut across the stepping stones.

START HERE

A gnome points you in the wrong direction. Move back 3 spaces.

Slide down the swan's neck to move on 2 spaces.

Miss a turn while you feed the fish.

You get a boost from a snack of flies – move on 1 space.

SPINNER

Cut around the dotted line and pierce the middle of your spinner with a toothpick.

To take a spin, hold the toothpick upright on the playing surface and spin it between your thumb and forefinger. When the spinning stops, the number at the top is the number of lily pads your frog is allowed to hop.

You catch a lift on a dragonfly. Move forward 3 spaces.

...e a shortcut ...down the ...waterfall.

A duck steals your breakfast. Miss a turn.

GOOD HOPPING!

FINISH HERE

You stop to make a crown of lilies. Miss a turn.

Everyone else's lily pads sink – they all miss a turn!

Your feet get tangled in reeds. Move back 3 spaces.

BACK OF SPINNER

Fill the page with rainbows and
pretty birds.

TREASURE HUNT

Take part in a treasure hunt that will have you racing all over the park!

This treasure hunt works using numbers and letters called co-ordinates. To use each co-ordinate clue, place your finger on the letter given. Move along the row to the column that matches the number. In that square you will find a new co-ordinate clue. Keep following the clues and finding the co-ordinates until you land in a square with a symbol instead of a co-ordinate. Use the key at the bottom to work out where the treasure is hidden, then turn to page 187 to check your answer. The first clue for the treasure hunt is at E3.

HOST A POP-STAR CONTEST

Are you ready for some all-singing, all-dancing fun?
Invite friends and family to join in as judges, performers
and audience members, and shine like a star.

Start by choosing the perfect place for performances – you'll need
a doorway for stylish entrances, a 'stage' area with plenty of
room for performers to show their best moves, and a
space opposite for the judges to sit. Don't forget to leave
some space for your audience.

BACKSTAGE PASSES

You also need a 'backstage' area for the performers to
prepare – your bedroom would be ideal. They will need
room to change into their costumes, mirrors to check
their star-style make-up, space to practise their
moves, and drinks and snacks to help them relax.

JUST JUDGING

Parents and grandparents make perfect contest judges.
Persuade up to four of them to join in, prepare a score
sheet for each person, with a column for each of the
categories shown below. Categories are scored out of ten,
with a total score out of 50:

Name	Styling	Singing	Dancing	Interview	Total

A WINNING PERFORMANCE.

To be sure of winning, contestants need to put on the best possible show for the judges. Here's how to get an outstanding score in each category:

Name:
Lots of well-known performers have stage names. For instance, Sandra Smith is a lovely name, but Sandrine Star is definitely a 10-out-of-10 superstar name. Come up with your own to really impress the judges.

Styling:
The judges must score each act on her overall costume – including her outfit, hair and make-up, if used. Try to choose outfits with as much sparkle as possible. Shiny fabrics will stand out particularly well. Add glittery make-up if you have any, and make your hair as gorgeous as possible.

Singing And Dancing:
Remember to choose a song you are familiar with, so you don't forget the words. Dance routines should be kept simple, so you don't get too out of breath to sing! The judges will still be wowed as long as you keep moving.

Interview:
The judges should ask each contestant a series of questions about her performance. Plan some answers in advance to avoid going blank, and remember to look the judges in the eye.

Top Tip. The judges should reveal the top three scores in reverse order for maximum suspense. The winner closes the contest with a final performance of her winning song.

BEACH BEAUTY

You're armed with your towel, shades, sunscreen and snorkel.
You're ready to have a splashing time at the seaside,
but a girl has her image to think of. So follow these handy hints
to be a beautiful beach babe.

SUMMER HAIR

Fun on the beach can be a nightmare for your hair – the sun and sea water will dry it out.

Keep your locks feeling silky and fight the frizz, by slicking lots of leave-in conditioner on to your hair and comb it through. If your hair is long enough, pull it into a ponytail for extra protection.

Everyone knows sunscreen is essential for anyone venturing out in the sun, but there's nothing worse than a red, sunburnt parting. Always keep the top of your head protected with a hat. Alternatively, tie a headscarf, with the ends behind your head for a super-stylish coverup.

SURFER STYLE

Surfer girls' hair always looks beautifully messy, 'tousled' by fun in the sun, sea and sand.

If you don't get to the beach, you can get the surfer-girl-hair look by mixing two tablespoons of salt in half a litre of warm water. Pour it over your hair after shampooing and don't rinse it out. This salty rinse will give your hair a cool beach-babe look.

WORKING THE WAVES

If it is long enough, wear your hair in plaits all day at the beach. In the evening brush your hair loose for soft, glamorous waves.

SUMMER FEET

Summer is the time to be bold, so paint your toenails with some bright polish.

Why not try painting each nail a different shade? Or, for a truly eye-catching look, use a dark colour first and then add a stripe of a different colour down the middle of each nail.

For super-soft summer feet, put on lots of moisturiser all over your feet before bedtime. Pop on a pair of old socks to protect your bed covers. This helps to keep moisture locked in to the skin of your feet, making them extra soft.

Getting sand between your toes can be annoying, but walking barefoot on the beach rubs away dead skin, leaving the soles of your feet feeling lovely and smooth.

AT THE SEASIDE

Complete these seaside-themed puzzles
and turn to page 187 to check your answers.

Which four of the details below are from the picture of the rockpool?

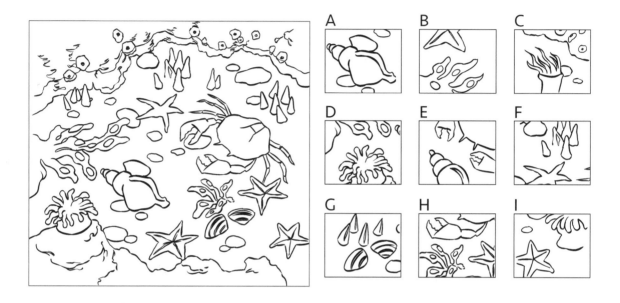

Which two of these ice-cream sundaes are identical?

Look at these beach volleyball players.

A. How many of the players are wearing shorts?

B. How many have at least one arm in the air?

C. How many are wearing flip-flops?

D. How many are wearing sunglasses?

Design daring sails for these boats.

CAMPFIRE TWISTS

It's time to get cooking by the campfire.

These delicious treats are perfect to bake over a campfire. You don't need to measure out the ingredients, and you don't even need any cooking utensils.

1. Make a pile of flour and scoop out the centre to form a well.

2. Pour a little water into the well, and mix together with your hands until you have a lump of dough. Don't worry if it gets messy. Add more flour or water if you need to.

3. Shape the dough with your hands into a large square.

4. Sprinkle lots of chocolate chips onto the middle of the dough, then fold it so that all the chocolate chips are on the inside.

5. Roll out the dough into a long sausage shape.

6. Twist the dough around a skewer or stick and toast over the glowing embers of your campfire.

What are we cooking on the campfire?

FUTURE FANTASTIC!

What will your future look like? Peer into a crystal ball and make your predictions. It's said that if you write your goals down you're more likely to achieve them, so get started on making your dream future a reality!

In ten years time I will be a _____.

I will be living in _____ with _____.

My greatest achievement will be _____

_____.

I will be on my way to becoming a _____

_____.

My best friend will be _____ and

the thing we will most enjoy doing will be

_____.

RAINY-DAY DECISIONS

Don't worry if it's raining – this fortune finder contains loads of great ideas for how to fill the time if you're stuck inside.

HOW TO MAKE IT

1. Cut around the fortune finder on the opposite page. Fold one corner over to the other to make a triangle, so that the writing is on the outside.

2. Fold your triangle in half again to form a smaller triangle. Then unfold the sheet and lie it flat.

4. Turn the fortune finder over and repeat step **3**, folding the new corners into the middle.

5. Fold the fortune finder in half from edge to edge, so the colours remain on the outside.

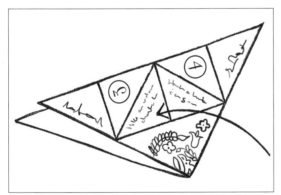

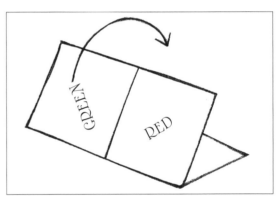

3. Fold each corner of the sheet into the middle, so the corners all meet at the centre of the sheet.

6. Unfold and fold in half the other way.

7. Slide the thumbs and forefinger of both hands under the flaps of the fortune finder, and find your fortune!

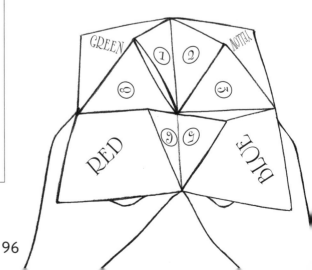

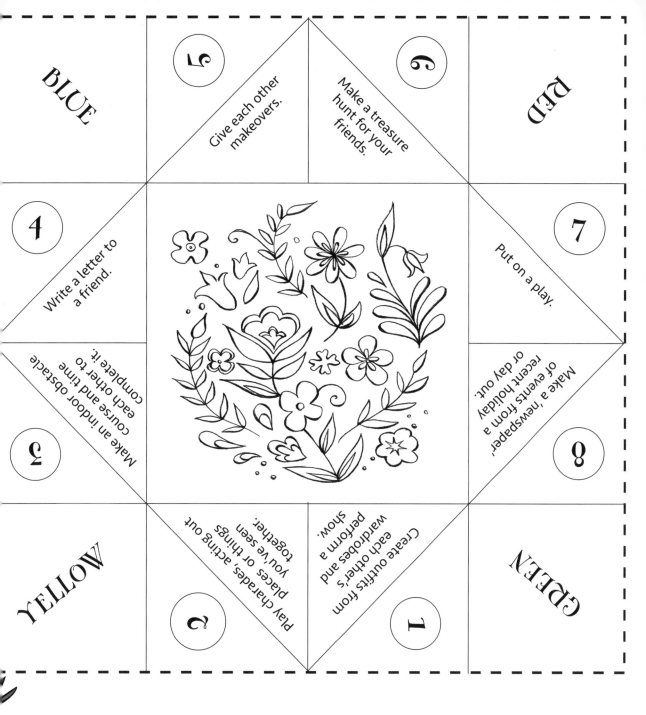

BLUE

RED

YELLOW

GREEN

5 — Give each other makeovers.

6 — Make a treasure hunt for your friends.

4 — Write a letter to a friend.

7 — Put on a play.

3 — Make an indoor obstacle course and time each other to complete it.

8 — Make a 'newspaper' of events from a recent holiday or day out.

2 — Play charades, acting out places or things you've seen together.

1 — Create outfits from each other's wardrobes and perform a show.

WHAT TO DO NEXT

Now ask a friend to choose a colour from the outside flaps. Spell out the colour, opening and closing the fortune finder for each letter. Holding the fortune finder open, ask your friend to pick one of the numbers shown inside. Count out the number and ask them to pick another one. Open up the flap beneath that number to reveal a rainy-day activity.

Fill the back of your fortune finder with flowers.

JOKE CORNER

Why is the sand wet?
Because the sea weed.

How does a mermaid travel around?
On an octobus.

Why were the elephants thrown
out of the swimming pool?
Because their trunks kept falling down.

What do you call a wicked old woman
who lives by the sea?
A sandwich.

SUPER SNAPS

Can you work out which girl took each of the photos below
at the summer garden party?

You'll need to think about where each photographer is standing, and which girl
she is aiming her camera at. Check your answers on page 187.

MAP MAYHEM

In map reading, combinations of letters and numbers are known as co-ordinates and refer to locations on the map. To use a co-ordinate, place your finger on the number given. Trace your finger along the row to the column that matches the letter. In that square you will find the symbol that the co-ordinates refer to.

Can you find the symbols at the following co-ordinates and use the key to find out what they mean? Check your answers on page 188.

1. 5A   **2.** 4E   **3.** 1F   **4.** 3B   **5.** 6D   **6.** 3G

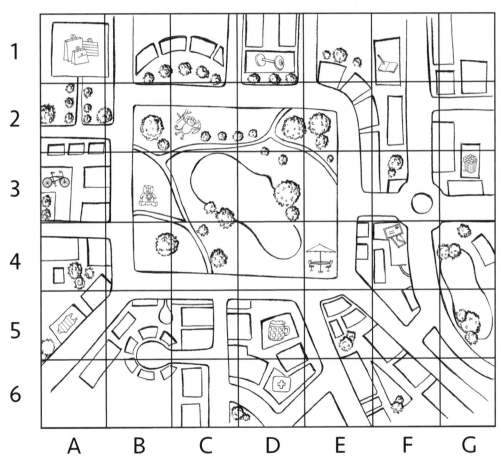

KEY

pub   gym   hospital   post office   school   swimming pool

shopping centre   zoo   café   theme park   bike hire   cinema

WHAT'S YOUR SUMMER STYLE?

Answer A, B, C or D to the questions below, then find out which summer style suits you best on the next page.

---

1. Your friend turns up at your house unexpectedly. What are you wearing?

A. A tracksuit and trainers

B. A spa-style dressing gown

C. Your new dress

D. A pair of customized jeans

---

4. Which of the following best describes your ideal perfume?

A. Fresh and fruity

B. Deep and musky

C. The newest one in the shop

D. A mixture of your favourite essential oils

---

2. What is your favourite way to spend a summer afternoon?

A. Playing frisbee in the park

B. Relaxing on a sun-lounger

C. Going for a picnic with a friend

D. Working on a craft project

---

5. What kind of bag do you pack for a sleepover?

A. Your gym bag

B. An oversized beach bag

C. A small, stylish suitcase

D. The bag you made last weekend

---

3. What is your favourite summer breakfast?

A. Scrambled eggs and orange juice

B. Yogurt with fruit and honey

C. Croissants with butter and jam

D. Home-made muesli

---

6. What is your summer hairstyle?

A. A ponytail

B. A glamorous blow-dry

C. You like to change your hairstyle regularly

D. Accessorized hairstyle with lots of grips/hairbands etc

WHAT YOUR ANSWERS MEAN

Count up how many of each letter you have chosen. Now look below to work out what your answers say about your style. If you scored an even mix of letters, this means you have a totally unique summer style – you go girl!

MOSTLY A: SPORTS SUPERSTAR

You're an active girl who's always bursting with energy. You like to spend time outside and love meeting up with your friends to play team games.You're super-fit and always have a healthy glow. Why not turn to pages 128 and 129 to find out how to make up your own street-dance routine?

MOSTLY B: GORGEOUS GODDESS

For you, the summer holidays are all about taking time out to pamper yourself. Your bedroom could compete with any of the top spas. You feel comfortable in any clothes – as long as your hair and skin are looking good you don't care! Turn to pages 44 and 45 for some summery beauty tips.

MOSTLY C: FASHIONABLE FRIEND

You love flicking through fashion magazines, and your friends look to you as someone who is always ahead of the latest trend. Turn to pages 162 and 163 to learn how to hold a Closet Swap Shop party.

MOSTLY D: CREATIVE KITTEN

You're an arty girl who likes to dress differently to your friends. You're brilliant at making the latest fashions your own and use the summer holidays to put your ideas into practice. Turn to pages 122 and 123 for a creative project that will last you all summer.

BAGS OF DIFFERENCE

Oh no! Your bag has been mixed up with someone else's at the airport.
Can you spot five differences between your bag (A) and the other bag?
Answers on page 188.

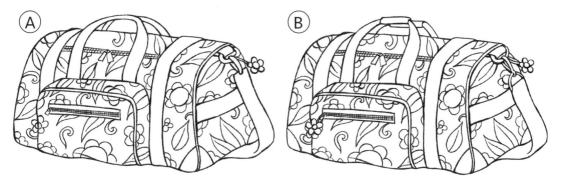

What have you packed in your suitcase?

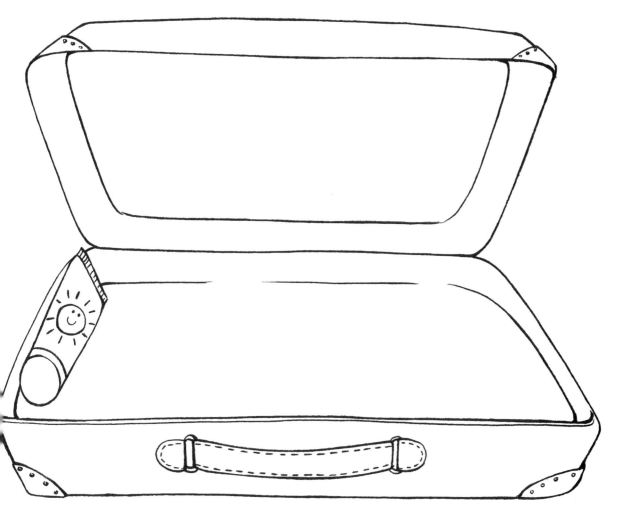

INDIAN HEADSCARF DANCE

Namaste! You can use any large scarf or shawl to do this dance routine – just put on some music and get dancing!

1. Start with the scarf draped over your shoulders and lightly grip the front edge.

Move your shoulders up and down in time with the music.

2. Lift your right arm up in the air and lower your left hand to your side.

Bend your knees and lean a little to your left.

3. Keeping your knees bent and your arms in position, turn to the left and walk round in a tight circle.

4. When you have turned a full circle, take your right arm over your head, and bring the scarf to the front. Lift your left arm up and take the scarf to the back again.

You should now be in the opposite position to step **2**.

Bend your knees and lean a little to your right.

5. Now walk round in a tight circle – to the right this time.

Take your left arm over your head, while raising your right arm up, and bring the scarf to the front.

104

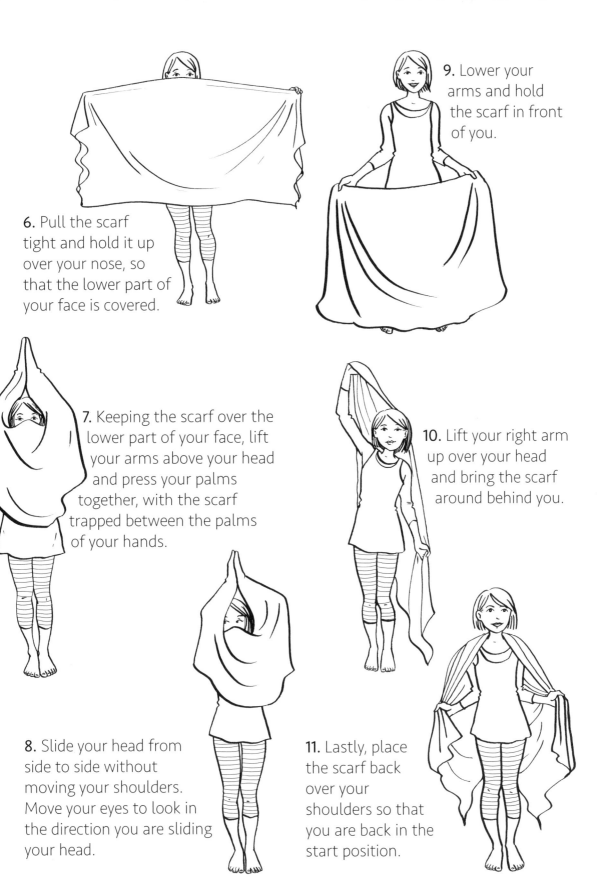

6. Pull the scarf tight and hold it up over your nose, so that the lower part of your face is covered.

9. Lower your arms and hold the scarf in front of you.

7. Keeping the scarf over the lower part of your face, lift your arms above your head and press your palms together, with the scarf trapped between the palms of your hands.

10. Lift your right arm up over your head and bring the scarf around behind you.

8. Slide your head from side to side without moving your shoulders. Move your eyes to look in the direction you are sliding your head.

11. Lastly, place the scarf back over your shoulders so that you are back in the start position.

SAND-CASTLE SURPRISE

Everyone wants to be queen of the castle, but this page will make sure it's you who wears the crown, with the best sand castle on the beach.

1. The perfect spot. Choose a site close enough to the sea so that you can easily get water, but not so close that your masterpiece will get washed away. Look for the point where the dark, wet sand starts to turn lighter.

2. Prepare the area. Pour buckets of water onto your chosen area and stamp down the sand until you have a firm area large enough for your sand castle.

3. Build a base. Build up a large mound of wet sand with a flat top. Pat down the sand as you build up the mound to create a firm, flat base for your sand castle.

4. Make the castle. Did you know that there's a scientific formula for building the perfect sand castle? Scientists have found that the winning recipe is $0.125 \times S = OW$, which basically means

Complete this sand castle.

that you should mix one bucket of water with eight buckets of sand to create the perfect sand mixture. Fill your buckets with the mixture, pat the sand down with your spade so that it's flat and compact, then carefully tip over the buckets on top of the mound. One large castle in the middle with four smaller 'turret' sand castles around it looks particularly impressive.

5. Make a moat and castle wall. A
moat is a deep trench filled with water that's built around a castle to protect it from attack. Dig out the sand at the base of your sand castle mound to create a trench that goes all the way around it.

Use the sand you've dug out to build up a wall around the outside of the trench. The wall should be about as tall as your hand and as wide as your wrist.

6. Fill the moat with water. Create a
trench that goes from the sea to your moat. Start by creating a passageway through the castle wall for the water to pass through. To do this, use your finger to carefully cut an arch into the area of the wall facing the sea. Next, dig a deep trench all the way from the archway to the sea. The sea water will rush down the trench towards your sand castle and fill the moat, guarding it from invaders and protecting your castle.

WATER WORLD

Complete the puzzles and turn to page 188 to check your answers.

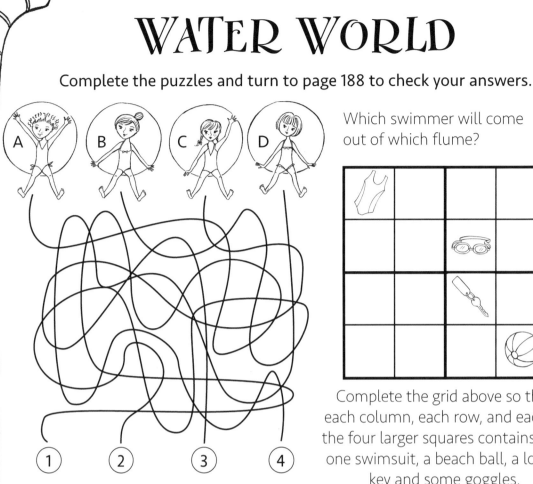

Which swimmer will come out of which flume?

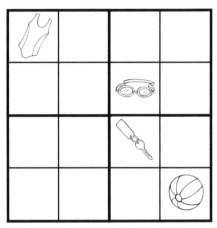

Complete the grid above so that each column, each row, and each of the four larger squares contains only one swimsuit, a beach ball, a locker key and some goggles.

Using only three straight lines, divide the swimming pool into six sections, with one swimmer and one beach ball in each.

108

Can you spot two identical burgers in this diner?

Can you find a clear path for this girl through the maze to the jacuzzi?

SUMMER PARTY PLANS

Throwing a tea party takes planning. Follow the advice below
to ensure your party day runs perfectly.

Send invitations. Choose some friends to invite to your tea party. Decide when and where you plan to hold the party and then fill in the invitations on the opposite page. Cut each one out and colour them in before handing them out to your friends.

Choose a menu. As well as baking cute cupcakes to serve (see pages 8 to 9), traditional tea-time foods also include dainty sandwiches, scones with jam, and cream cakes.

Choose a colour scheme. Choose two colours that go well together – for example, pink and blue or yellow and green. Pick a tablecloth to match your colour scheme and choose napkins in a contrasting colour.

Find flowers. Place a vase of flowers that work with your colour scheme in the centre of the table.

Be the hostess with the mostest. As your guests arrive, show them to the table and ask them to take a seat.

Tea alternative. Traditionally, people drink tea at tea parties. However, if you and your friends don't like the taste of tea, why not make a delicious 'watermelonade' drink? (See page 74 for a refreshing recipe.) Serve in pretty tea cups with matching saucers.

Once everyone has a drink and some food, take off your apron and join the party!

PRETTY PARTY INVITATIONS

Fill in the details on the invitation cards below, then carefully cut them out.

The letters RSVP appear at the bottom of each invitation – this is short for the French phrase 'répondez s'il vous plaît ' which means 'please would you reply'.

Dear: ....
You are invited to a summer tea party hosted by:
....
Location: ....
Date and Time: ....
RSVP

Dear: ....
You are invited to a summer tea party hosted by:
....
Location: ....
Date and Time: ....
RSVP

Dear: ....
You are invited to a summer tea party hosted by:
....
Location: ....
Date and Time: ....
RSVP

Dear: ....
You are invited to a summer tea party hosted by:
....
Location: ....
Date and Time: ....
RSVP

Dear: ....
You are invited to a summer tea party hosted by:
....
Location: ....
Date and Time: ....
RSVP

Dear: ....
You are invited to a summer tea party hosted by:
....
Location: ....
Date and Time: ....
RSVP

Colour in each invitation before handing them out to your friends.

Fill the page with delicious fruits.

GLAM UP YOUR GIFTS

Want an easy way to give your giftwrap the 'wow' factor?
Check out these cool ideas to make sure your presents really stand out.

PRETTY PAPERS

To achieve this simple, yet sophisticated look, first wrap each present in a single shade of giftwrap – the brighter the better.

Next, cut a wide strip of pretty, patterned paper in a contrasting shade that fits around the gift, leaving just a bit of the plain paper showing on either side.

Finally, tie a thin ribbon around the middle of the patterned strip for the perfect finishing touch to your seriously glamorous gifts.

THINK OUTSIDE THE BOX

Bored of store-bought giftwrap? Get creative and think of other materials you could use to cover your gifts and make them really original. Here are some ideas to get you started:

• Wrap a framed holiday photo in a map of the place where it was taken.

• Tie shampoos and bubble baths into a luxury bundle using a bright headscarf.

• Cover CDs or concert tickets in sheet music for an extra-funky feel.

RADICAL RIBBONS

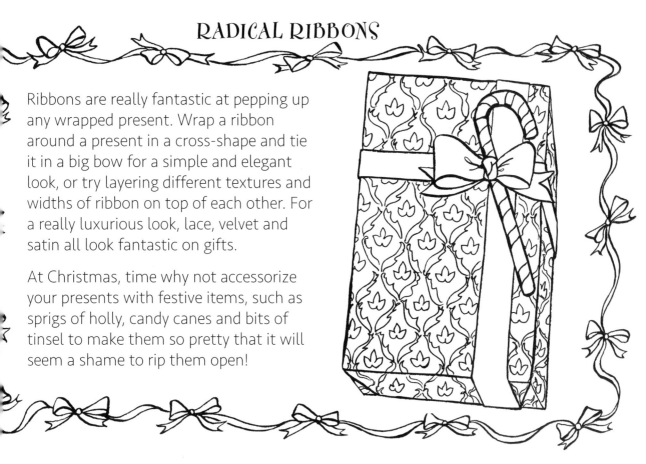

Ribbons are really fantastic at pepping up any wrapped present. Wrap a ribbon around a present in a cross-shape and tie it in a big bow for a simple and elegant look, or try layering different textures and widths of ribbon on top of each other. For a really luxurious look, lace, velvet and satin all look fantastic on gifts.

At Christmas, time why not accessorize your presents with festive items, such as sprigs of holly, candy canes and bits of tinsel to make them so pretty that it will seem a shame to rip them open!

Make these gifts gorgeous with paper, bows and ribbons.

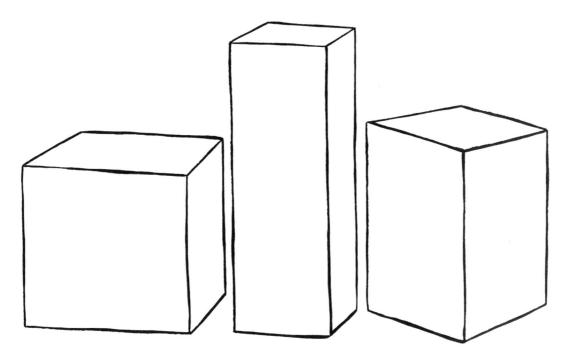

SUPERB SCIENTISTS

Roll up your sleeves and turn your kitchen into a laboratory with these excellent experiments.

SUPER SUGAR ROCKS

In this experiment, you can make your own scientific sugar lolly from a 'supersaturated' solution of sugar.

You will need:
• an empty jam jar, with lid
• a piece of string, 15 cm long
• a bag of white sugar.

Warning: Always ask an adult to help you when you need to use the kettle.

Sugar is a substance that is soluble in a liquid. This means that when it is added to water, it dissolves. The water becomes sugary, and there are no sugar granules left. The liquid is now a solution. There's a limit to how much sugar can be dissolved in a glass of water though, and when this limit is reached, the solution is saturated.

However, there's something you can do to get more sugar into a solution: add heat.

To see this in action, ask an adult to help you boil the kettle, then fill your jam jar with hot water. The jar will be hot, so ask the adult to hold it steady for you with a cloth or an oven glove.

Now it's time to add the sugar. See if you can guess how many teaspoons of sugar will dissolve in the hot water. Add a spoonful at a time, and stir until it dissolves.

When no more sugar will dissolve, lower your piece of string into the water, so that the end hangs over the rim of the jar. Trap it with the jar lid, and leave the jar in a safe place.

As the solution cools, the extra sugar will not be able to stay dissolved, and sugar crystals will start to form on the string.

After a week, you will have a delicious sugar lolly! Yum.

SHE'S ELECTRIC!

Use this experiment to create your own static electricity.

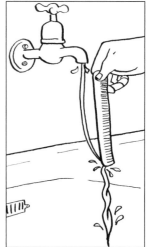

You will need:

• a plastic comb • running water.

Everything in the world is made of atoms – tiny particles that are too small to see. Inside each atom, there are even smaller particles: protons, neutrons and electrons. Protons have a positive electrical charge. Neutrons are neutral – they have no charge. Electrons are negatively charged.

Most of the time, atoms have no charge. However, if you rub two objects together, you can create a charge that makes the electrons move from one atom to another. This charge is static electricity.

To do this yourself, simply run your comb through your hair a few times. This will make negatively charged electrons jump from your hair to the comb. The comb will now have a negative charge.

Now run a very thin stream of water and hold the charged comb close to it. The water will be attracted to the comb and 'bend' towards it!

SOAP-TASTIC!

Discover how gas expands when heated with this incredible experiment.

Warning: Make sure you ask an adult for help with the microwave in this experiment.

You will need:

• a bar of soap • a microwave • a microwaveable bowl.

Note. A bar of soap that has lots of tiny air bubbles in it – one that floats in the bath, for example – will work best for this experiment.

Remove any stickers from the soap and place it in the bowl in the microwave. Heat for two minutes on full power, watching all the time to see what happens. As the soap gets hotter, the gas inside the bubbles – air – expands and the solid bar of soap will foam up out of the bowl. Amazing!

Allow the soap to cool for at least five minutes before you touch it. Clean the microwave before anyone cooks food in it.

FASHIONISTA FUN

SPOT THE FASHIONISTAS

Can you find the two girls below in the crowd?
Answers on page 188.

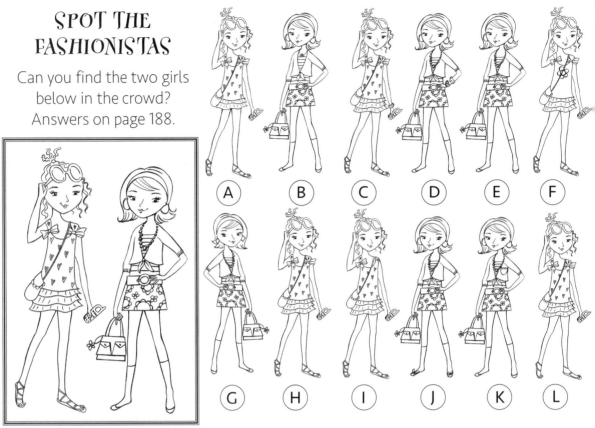

A B C D E F

G H I J K L

Decorate these flip-flops.

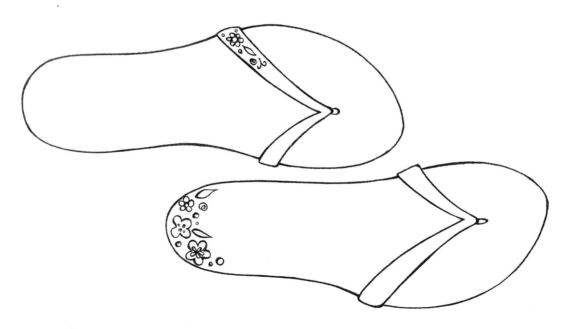

DANCE AROUND THE WORLD

Can you match each dance style to its country of origin? Fill in your answers in the spaces below, then check to see if you are right on page 188.

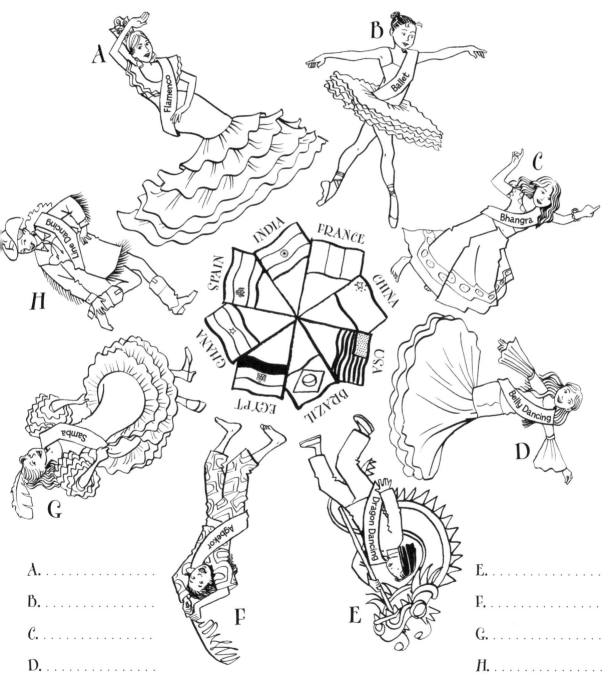

A. . . . .

B. . . . .

C. . . . .

D. . . . .

E. . . . .

F. . . . .

G. . . . .

H. . . . .

FASHION FRENZY

Backstage at a fashion show things aren't going well.
Can you solve the problems and help the show run smoothly?
Check your answers on page 189.

MODEL MATCH

These models are meant to be walking down the catwalk with dogs in their handbags, but their bags have all been muddled up. Follow the leads to find out which bag belongs to which model.

These models are due on the catwalk in three minutes – can you help them find their missing shoes to complete the matching pairs? Which poor model doesn't have a matching pair?

MAKE-UP MAYHEM

The make-up artist has just had a tantrum and quit! Quick, use colouring pencils to give these models makeovers that match the theme of their shows.

Hollywood Glamour

8os Retro

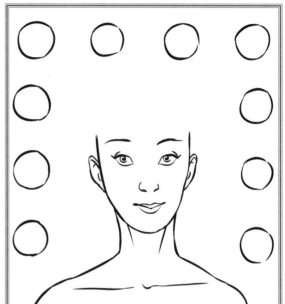

Vampire Chic

Natural Beauty

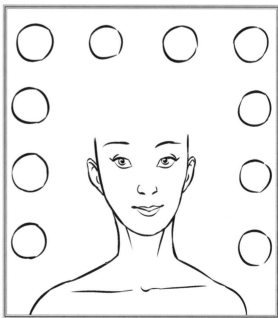

SEW ... FANTASTIC!

The long summer holidays are the perfect opportunity to get creative.

Add colour and texture to your bedroom with a range of scatter cushions made from different fabrics. Here's how to make your own.

For each cushion you will need:

- an old cushion • a length of fabric (big enough to wrap around the cushion)
- thread in a colour that matches your fabric • a needle • scissors • sewing pins
- beads, buttons and so on to decorate • old newspaper • 2 lengths of ribbon.

1. Cut out a piece of fabric that is roughly twice the size of the cushion, leaving an extra 5 cm of width around the edges.

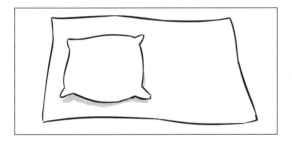

2. Fold the fabric in half, as shown below.

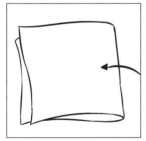

3. Fix sewing pins along the outside edges of the fabric to hold it together. Leave one side of your square unpinned.

4. Thread your needle using roughly 1½ m of thread. Tie a double knot in the end of it. Push the needle through one corner, closest to the fold of the cushion cover. Pull through on the other side of the knot.

5. Pull the needle back through the fabric about 1½ cm ahead of your original point and again, gently pull the thread through.

Once you have done this, push the needle back through the fabric in the same point that you started. Pull the thread through. Now push the needle through the fabric again, roughly 1 cm ahead of the last point, as shown below.

6. Continue sewing in this way in a straight line until you are about 1½ cm from the next corner.

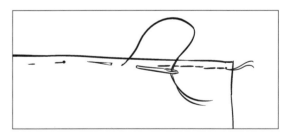

7. Rotate the fabric a quarter turn and sew along the next edge as you did in step **5**.

8. When you reach the next corner of the cushion cover, secure your stitches by sewing over the same spot ten times. Cut off any excess thread.

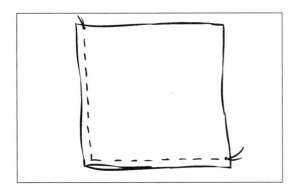

9. Turn the cushion cover right side out and place a piece of newspaper inside it – this will stop you sewing through both sides of the fabric in the next step.

10. Decorate one side of the cushion cover by stitching on buttons, beads, sequins and coloured feathers to create your own design. Remove the newspaper when you are done.

11. Insert the old cushion inside the cover along the open end.

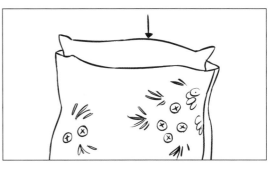

12. Carefully use the scissors to make two snips in the top layer of fabric. The snips should divide the open end into thirds, and be about 2 cm from the edge of the fabric. Make identical snips in the same places on the bottom layer of fabric.

13. Use the lengths of ribbon to close the cushion by tying the top layer of fabric to the bottom layer. Secure with a bow.

14. Make as many cushions as you like and scatter them over your bed, or give as presents to your friends and family.

Draw your dream holiday destination.

HOLIDAY HERO

'OK, I'll come, but I'm not getting wet!'

'Just get on the boat, Amrita, and please try and look like you're enjoying yourself,' begged Amrita's mum.

Amrita looked over her shoulder at her friends playing on the beach. It was so unfair! She was terrified of the sea. When she was little she'd been knocked over by a huge wave and banged her head.

Taking care not to look at the waves swelling either side of the boat, she jumped in. Inside there were rows of orange plastic seats and it smelled of fish. This was not her idea of fun.

Other people started to board the boat, laughing and taking photos. Amrita sat down, refusing to look at her mum or her sister, Sophia, as they passed.

The engine started and, with a giant rumble, the boat pulled away. With tears in her eyes Amrita looked out of the back window, and watched as her friends disappeared in the distance.

Half an hour later the boat stopped and there was a great commotion as people rummaged through the boat's supply of flippers, snorkels and masks. Sophia was floating in her rubber ring laughing as a group of children splashed around her.

Amrita moved to the other side of the boat so that she wouldn't have to see everyone having fun without her. She saw a young boy wearing a rubber ring in the water. She realised he was being dragged away from the boat by the current. He was crying and waving his arms. Amrita knew that she had to get help before he disappeared out of sight, but there was no-one else on the boat.

'Help,' she cried, but no-one could hear her. She rushed out onto the deck. 'It's OK,' she called to the boy. 'I'm coming.'

Amrita's heart was pounding, but she didn't have time to think. She jumped in fully clothed. Everything she'd learnt at swimming lessons came rushing back to her, and she swam towards the boy.

'Are you alright?' she shouted to him when she got close, but the boy just kept crying. Quickly, she began to pull him by the rubber ring back towards the boat, but it was really hard work.

She saw that a crowd had gathered on the boat, and people were swimming towards her. A man got there first.

'Thank you, thank you,' he said, as he took the boy from Amrita. 'This is my son, and no-one knew what had happened to him. He just disappeared.'

When they arrived back at the boat everyone was cheering and clapping.

'You're a hero, Amrita,' said her mum. 'I'm so proud of you – I bet you can't wait to tell your friends all about it.'

THEATRELAND

It's premiere night at the theatre – are you red-carpet ready?
The answers are on page 189.

Which photo has been taken by which person as the actors walk the red carpet?
Think about the way the cameras are pointing to help you work out your answers.

WHO'S THE LEADING LADY?

Can you spot ten differences between the female lead and her stunt double?

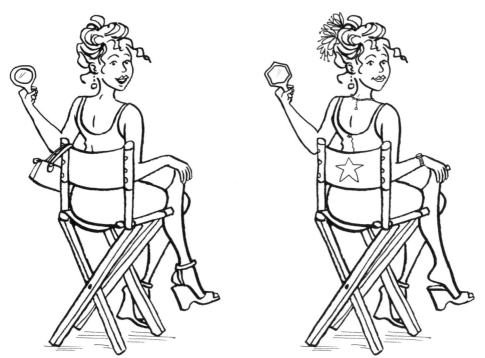

AUTOGRAPH HUNTER

Can you find your way backstage to get an autograph from the lead actor?

STEP IT UP

When the mood takes you and you feel like dancing,
why not make up your very own street-dance routine?

POP ON YOUR DANCING SHOES

To get started, slip on some loose clothes – tracksuit bottoms, a T-shirt and your favourite trainers are ideal. Take a portable music player outside and turn on your favourite dance track. Now you are ready to have a go at these sassy street-dance moves. You can create your own cool routine by mixing up the moves below, in whichever order you choose. Once you've got the hang of it, why not have a competition with your friends and battle it out to see who's got the best moves? You can even throw your own signature street-dance move in to the mix!

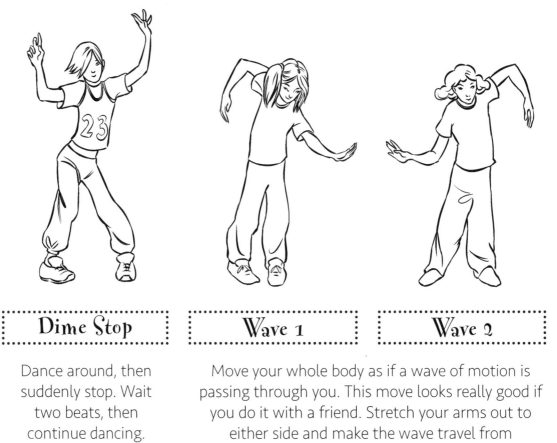

Dime Stop

Wave 1

Wave 2

Dance around, then suddenly stop. Wait two beats, then continue dancing.

Move your whole body as if a wave of motion is passing through you. This move looks really good if you do it with a friend. Stretch your arms out to either side and make the wave travel from fingertip to fingertip, as above.

The Robot

Dance using stiff, precise movements – as if you're a robot.

The Swag

Sway your arms in time to the music, while walking on the spot.

Drop It

With your hands above your head, bend your knees and drop all the way to the floor, then 'pop' back up without pausing.

Pop-Lock Walk

Imagine your arms and legs are connected with string so that when you lift your right arm up your right leg also lifts and vice versa.

Heel-Toe Flick

Bend your knees and turn your feet out so that your heels are facing each other. On the next beat of the music, turn your feet in so the toes are now facing each other. Repeat.

Running Girl

Run on the spot while bending your arms up to your chest. As you run, straighten your arms out in front of you in time to the music.

HAWAIIAN LUAU

Aloha! Let's party, Hawaiian-style! Once you've
worked these puzzles out, check your answers on page 189.

You've been invited to a traditional Hawaiian luau party. Follow the instructions on the invitation to find your way there. Is the party at the Shark Cove Café, the Halona Blowhole or the Diamond Lighthouse?

Come To Our Party this Saturday at 3 p.m.

To get to there, start in the middle of the West Coast Beach and head east. Turn left at the T-junction, then turn immediately right. Turn right again, then take the second left. Turn left, then take the first right – walk straight ahead and you'll arrive at the party.

West Coast Beach

Shark Cove Café

Halona Blowhole

Diamond Lighthouse

SUDOKU
HAWAIIAN-STYLE

Complete the grid so that each row, each column and each outlined block of four squares contains only one heart, one turtle, one flower and one sun.

LUSCIOUS LUAU SMOOTHIES

Can you spot which of these tropical fruit smoothies is yours? The one you're looking for has a cocktail stick with at least one cherry on it. It has a cocktail umbrella and is in a tall glass, but does not have a straw.

PARADISE DIVIDE

Can you draw two straight lines across the beach to divide it into four areas? Each area must have one palm tree and one tiki torch in it.

A RAINY DAY ADVENTURE

Maria pressed her face up against the window and looked out miserably.

It had been raining for twelve days in a row, and she was bored, bored, bored.

'Come here, Maria,' said her grandmother. 'I have something to tell you that I think will cheer you up.'

Maria brightened, glad of anything that might be interesting.

A grandmother's wisdom

'You might be bored now, Maria, but there will be a full moon tonight. Did you know that if you look into a puddle at midnight, you will see your future in the light cast by a full moon?'

Now that didn't sound boring at all! That sounded like exactly the kind of adventure Maria had been dreaming about ever since it had started raining.

Maria called her friend Amelie at once, and they hatched a plan. Half an hour later, Amelie was standing on Maria's

door in her mackintosh and wellington boots, ringing the doorbell.

Maria pulled her friend into the house. 'I've set the alarm clock for 11.30 p.m.,' Maria informed her excitedly, 'and I've prepared a midnight feast for us to snack on before we head out to discover our future.'

Amelie looked at Maria and raised one eyebrow. 'It's going to be a fun adventure, but you don't believe that rubbish do you?'

'We'll see,' replied Maria, with a knowing smile. Her grandmother had never been wrong about anything like this before.

The girls got ready for bed and spent at least an hour whispering and giggling before sleep finally took hold of them and they drifted off.

Brrrring, brrrring, brrrring!

The alarm brought the girls awake, and they jumped

132

out of bed and tucked into the feast that Maria had prepared.

When they were full, Maria and Amelie pulled waterproofs on over their nightclothes and headed out into the pouring rain.

'Come on,' said Maria, taking hold of her friend's hand and pulling her into the garden. 'The water always pools over here, so there will be a perfect puddle for us to look into.'

As they stood over the puddle, the rain clouds parted, and the full moon shone through, illuminating the girls in an eerie white light. They held on tight to each other's hands and cautiously peered down into the puddle.

A mysterious reflection

Looking up out of the puddle they saw two smiling ladies, who were also holding hands, peering back at them. The girls stared in shocked silence as one of the ladies started to speak.

'Oh, my dears, you're so young!'

She turned to look at her friend, saying, 'Remember when that was us, peering into this puddle?' Her friend nodded.

'I didn't believe it was going to work, but it did. We discovered our future. We discovered that it would be full of fun and laughter and all the wonderful things that make up life.'

'And the most important thing we learned was that we would be there for each other through all of it – that we would be friends forever – even when we were much, much older.'

'But who are you both?' cried Maria.

'Dear girls, we're you, of course! This is your future.'

Always there

Maria and Amelie laughed and cried and hugged each other. 'Friends forever!' they declared in unison!

DESTINATION DETECTIVES

When you next go away, use your detective skills to search for clues about your holiday destination to help you answer the questions below.

Even if you're holidaying close to home you might find out some things you didn't know before. Wow your holiday companions with the fascinating facts you've found out, and impress the locals with how much you know about their culture.

What does the country's flag look like? Draw it here.

Draw a piece of art that you saw on holiday.

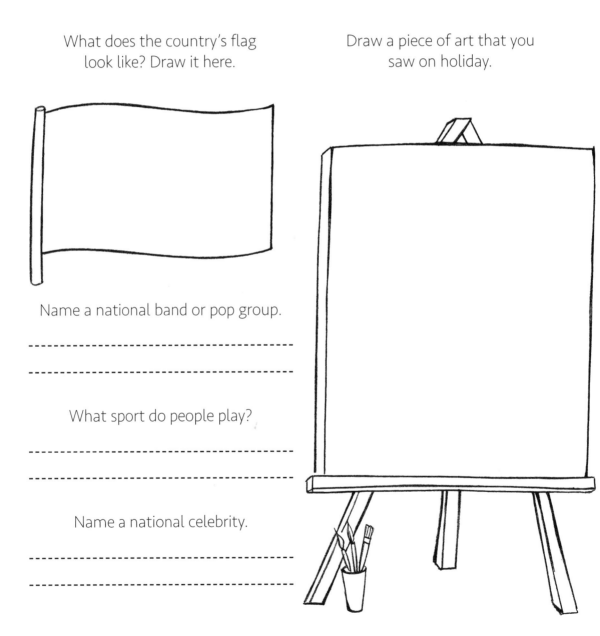

Name a national band or pop group.

What sport do people play?

Name a national celebrity.

Who is the leader of the country you're in?

What currency is used?

What does the national dress look like?

Find out the name of a festival that people celebrate in the country.

Draw a picture of the local dish.

List three tourist attractions you'd like to visit in the country.

What is the biggest difference between the place you are on holiday and home?

GET YOUR SKATES ON

The girls want to ice-skate to the snowmen they have made. You can tell which girl made which snowman by the matching pattern on their scarves. The girls can skate straight up, down and sideways, but not diagonally across the squares. Only one girl can pass through each square. Can you work out a route for each girl? The first one has been done for you. You can find the answers on page 190.

FRIENDOMETER

Each description below is worth a certain number of Friendship Points. Read each one, and, if the sentence describes you perfectly, you can shade in the number of points shown, starting from the bottom of your Friendometer. How close to the top can you get?

HOW GOOD A FRIEND ARE YOU?

• I don't get jealous if my friends are friends with other people.
4 Friendship Points

• A friend can tell me if she's feeling worried.
2 Friendship Points

• I always remember my friends' birthdays.
2 Friendship Points

• I would help a friend with homework.
2 Friendship Points

• I like to make little gifts for my friends.
2 Friendship Points

• I'd lend a friend my prettiest top.
1 Friendship Point

• I often give my friends compliments.
2 Friendship Points

• My friends describe me as trustworthy.
2 Friendship Points

• I don't talk about friends behind their backs.
3 Friendship Points

• I've never broken a promise to a friend.
4 Friendship Points

• I would give a friend my last sweet.
1 Friendship Point

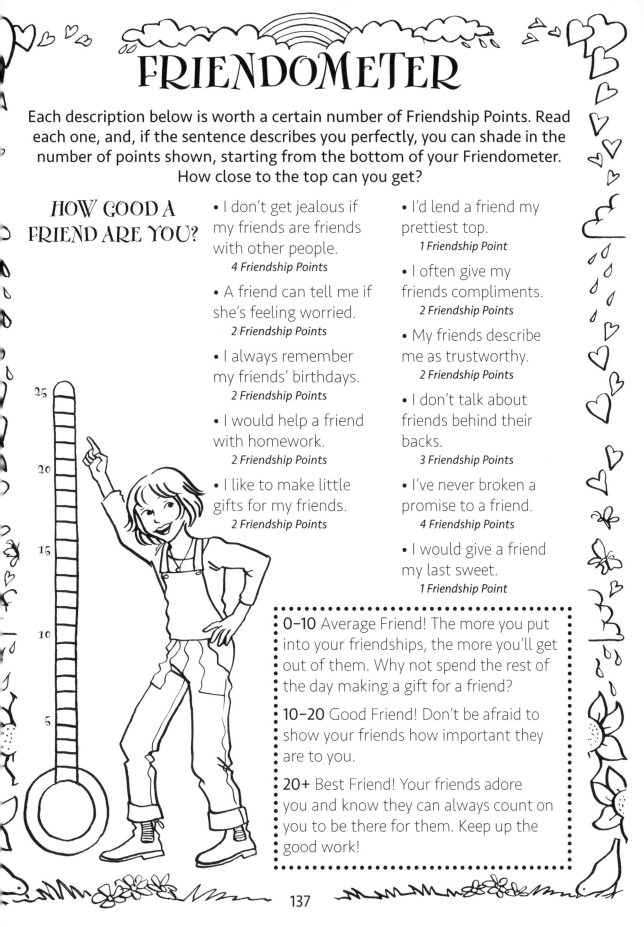

0–10 Average Friend! The more you put into your friendships, the more you'll get out of them. Why not spend the rest of the day making a gift for a friend?

10–20 Good Friend! Don't be afraid to show your friends how important they are to you.

20+ Best Friend! Your friends adore you and know they can always count on you to be there for them. Keep up the good work!

BRAIN-BASHERS

See how quickly you can complete these logical puzzles without your brain exploding! Record how long it takes you to work out each one in the spaces provided. You'll find the answers on page 190.

TROPHY TIME

Three friends, Emily, Alyssa and Preeya, are discussing how many football trophies a boy in their class, named Alex, has won. Only one of them is correct – the other two are wrong. Can you work out who by studying their conversation?

'Alex is so sweet, and he's won more than one football trophy,' said Emily.

'He's won at least five!' Alyssa scoffed.

Preeya interrupted, saying, 'I heard that it's an even number.'

How many trophies has Alex won?

Time: . . . .

SUNFLOWER SUMS

Alice is growing a sunflower that doubles in height every day. After 30 days, the sunflower will be as tall as she is. After how many days would the sunflower be half her height?

Time: . . . .

SUMMER FUN

Summer's mum has four children. The first child is called April, the second child is called May, and the third child is called June. What is the name of the fourth child?

Time: . . . .

DONKEY DILEMMA

Can you move just one toothpick to make the donkey change position?

Time: . . . .

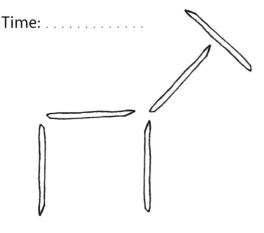

CHOCOLATE CONUNDRUM

Rebecca has bought three boxes of chocolates for her friends: white chocolates for Kate, milk chocolates for Sarah, and a mixture of milk and white chocolates for Bella. However, the chocolate labels have been mixed up, and the boxes all look the same! None of the labels are correct.

Rebecca thinks she can shake a chocolate out of one box without tearing it, but how could she work out which label goes on which box by taking just one chocolate from one box?

Time: . . . .

WHO'S THE TOP?

Four friends are trying to decide who is the tallest – can you work it out just from these clues?

Louisa is only taller than Siân and Preeya is shorter than Sally. However, Preeya is taller than Siân, and Sally is taller than Louisa.

How tall are they? Tick one box for each of them.

Time: . . . .

	100 cm	105 cm	110 cm	115 cm
Louisa				
Siân				
Sally				
Preeya				

GO GREEN

Saving energy on your summer holiday will help save the planet.

Read the facts below to find out how you can go green on holiday, then follow the doodle instructions to make the house planet-friendly.

GREEN GUIDES

• Ask an adult to unplug electrical appliances when you leave home to save energy. Never leave them on standby (with a red light shining) as this uses up energy.

• Find out where the local bike-hire shop is and get cycling. Riding a bike is much better for the environment than using a car.

• Go green at the supermarket by encouraging your parents to only buy locally grown fruit and veg – not items that have been flown around the world. When you get home, why not grow your own fruit and veg in your garden or in a window box?

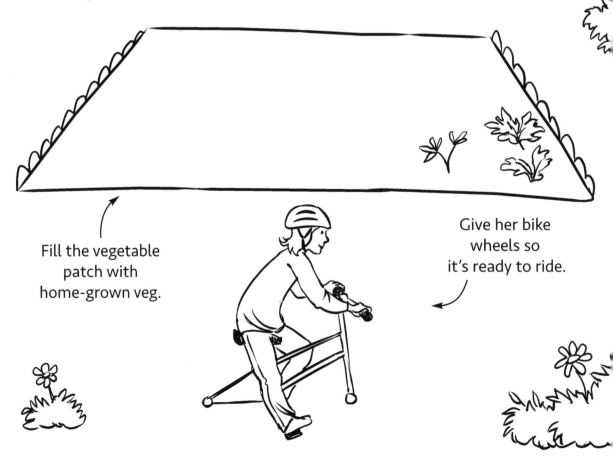

Fill the vegetable patch with home-grown veg.

Give her bike wheels so it's ready to ride.

• Save water by turning the taps off while you brush your teeth. Don't do any laundry on holiday – wait until you get home to do one big wash to save water.

• Recycling bottles, cans, paper and cardboard will mean your waste gets turned into something else, which saves energy. Ask at the local tourist information office to find out where the recycling bins are located.

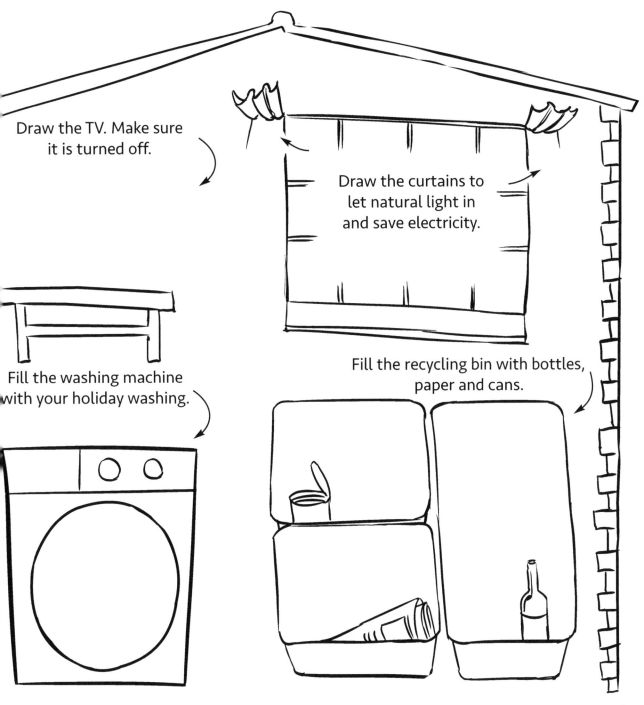

Draw the TV. Make sure it is turned off.

Draw the curtains to let natural light in and save electricity.

Fill the washing machine with your holiday washing.

Fill the recycling bin with bottles, paper and cans.

RELAXATION STATION

When you travel, getting stuck in traffic or hanging around at an airport or a station can be a real stress. These simple techniques will keep you and your family feeling relaxed and raring to go.

HEALING HANDS

You can perform this simple hand massage on a friend or family member anywhere – in the car, by the pool, in your bedroom or even in a café. Follow the steps below to pamper and relax your 'client'.

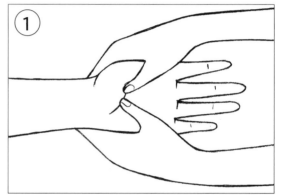

Step One. Ask your client to take off any rings before you start. Hold one of your client's hands palm upwards in both your hands. Your fingers should be underneath, and your thumbs on top. Use your thumbs to apply some pressure and make ten large circles over your client's palm.

Step Two. Take your client's hand in your left hand. Hold the bottom of their thumb with the thumb and index finger of your right hand. Slide your grip up to the top of their thumb. Gently squeeze the nail, then release. Do this three times and then repeat on each of their fingers.

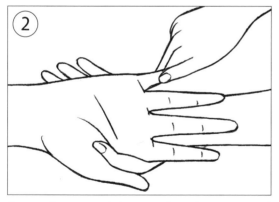

Step Three. Hold your client's wrist with your left hand, and interlock the fingers of your right hand with theirs, so that your palms are facing. Gently move your client's wrist round in a circle five times, first in one direction and then in the other direction. Finally, repeat **step one.**

Now begin the complete sequence again on the other hand.

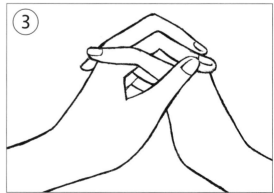

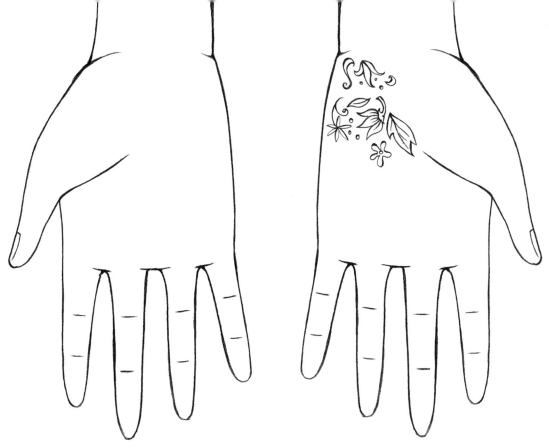

Can you decorate these hands with henna?

JOURNEY YOGA

On a long journey, stay cool and calm with these yoga moves that stretch tired muscles.

Sit with your bottom close to the front of your chair. Take three deep breaths, then perform these two moves.

Sunshine Stretch. Tuck your left foot underneath the chair and slide your right foot forward as far as it will go. Keeping your back straight and your left arm by your side, breathe in as you stretch your right arm up in front of you. Breathe out as you lower your arm, then repeat three times with each arm.

Chair Cat. Sit with your feet flat on the floor and your hands on your thighs. Stretch your body up and backwards so that you're looking at the ceiling, breathing out as you do so.

Now breathe in as you lean forward over your knees and stretch the back of your neck. Repeat five times.

SUMMER SPINNERS

Liven up your garden or window box with these special summer spinners.

You will need:

• three pieces of plain paper • a drawing pin
• a pencil with a rubber on the end • scissors • a glue stick • felt-tip pens.

1. Trace the pattern below on to two pieces of paper.

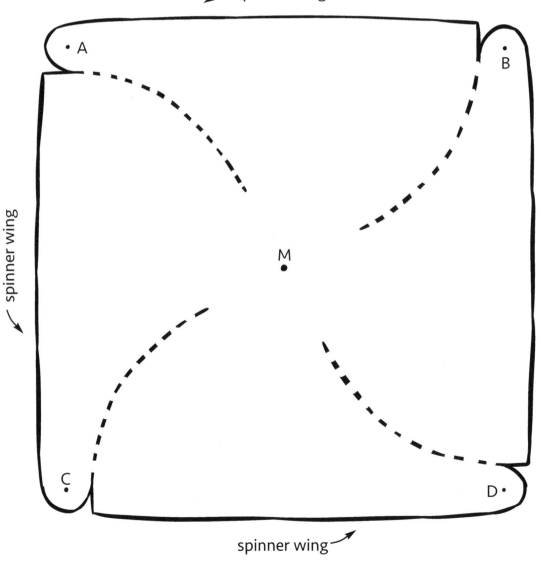

spinner wing

A

B

spinner wing

spinner wing

M

C

D

spinner wing

2. Carefully cut out each pattern along the solid lines.

3. Line up the two shapes so that they fit nicely back-to-back. Glue them together.

4. Using your felt-tip pens, doodle a different design on each side of the spinner shape – why not draw flowers and spots on one side and cherries and stripes on the other?

5. Trace the star shape below on to the third piece of paper.

Draw a dot in the middle of the star. Colour in the star shape and cut it out.

6. Carefully cut along the four dotted lines of the spinner shape.

7. Fold the corners of the spinner wings (the areas labelled **A**, **B**, **C** and **D**) into the middle of the spinner shape (**M**).

8. Use the drawing pin to carefully poke a hole through the dot in the centre of the star. Now pierce a hole through each of the spinner wings – each wing should now be pinned behind the star.

9. Carefully push the end of the pin into the side of the rubber on the end of the pencil.

10. Place on your windowsill or in your garden on a breezy summer's day and watch it spin and make pretty patterns.

Decorate these summer spinners.

145

Doodle a magical land through the wardrobe.

PUPPY POWER

Can you work out which puppy belongs to which girl?
The answers are on page 190.

Rosie

C

Leila

B

A

Caitlin

PERFECT POSTCARDS

This alternative to a diary is the perfect way to keep a record of everything that happens.

1. Buy a postcard each day of your holiday that reminds you of something that happened, or somewhere you went during the day.

2. Every evening, write a diary entry on the back of the day's postcard. Describe where you went and what you saw. You could get your holiday companions to add their comments, too.

3. When you get back from holiday, hole punch each postcard in the top left-hand corner. Make sure that you hole punch each one in the same place so that they line up properly.

4. Thread a piece of ribbon through each of the holes, and tie it in a bow at the top. You will now have a postcard book of holiday memories that will last a lifetime.

DID YOU KNOW?

One of these sizzling summer facts is not true.
Can you guess which one? The answer is on page 190.

FACT 1. The hottest place ever recorded on Earth was El Azizia in Libya. On 13th September 1922 the temperature reached 57.8 °C. Human muscles actually stop working at 50 °C, which makes it impossible to survive for long at these temperatures.

FACT 2. The world's most expensive ice-cream sundae is called the 'Frrrozen Haute Chocolate' and can be bought at the Serendipity 3 restaurant in New York. It costs $25,000 (£15,000) and is served with a golden spoon.

FACT 3. In many countries Midsummer's Day is traditionally celebrated with a bonfire that wards away evil spirits. According to ancient tradition, the healing power of herbs is strongest on this day, especially if picked at sunrise. Healers and witches would set out before dawn to gather herbs to use for the rest of the year.

FACT 4. Wearing dark colours keeps you cool. This is because light colours absorb heat, whereas dark colours reflect it.

FACT 5. In the part of Finland that is in the Arctic Circle, the sun doesn't set for 73 days during the summer.

FACT 6. The end of summer and not getting enough sunshine can cause an illness called 'SAD' (Seasonal Affective Disorder). It makes you feel tired and moody, and is treated with bright lights.

FACT 7. In 1952, a group of friends had a very unusual barbecue on a six-metre long grill. They cooked a fully-grown crocodile that had eaten an antelope. The antelope roasted inside the crocodile's stomach, and the friends enjoyed a mixed-meat feast served up with fresh mango.

FUN ON THE FARM

There's lots going on down on the farm in the summertime.
Complete these farmyard puzzles, then check your answers on page 191.

How many birds and how many apples can you spot in the orchard?

Can you spot five differences between the two horses with their foals?

Can you help the dog find his way home through the woods?

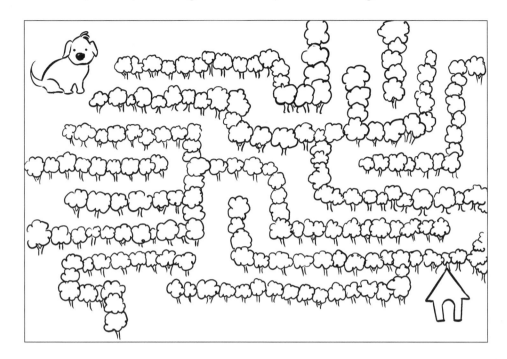

These cows are jealous of their stylish friend.
Give them a similar splodgy pattern.

JEAN GENIUS

Here's how to turn an
ordinary exercise book into
a stylish denim notebook.

You will need:

• an old pair of jeans (check with an adult that it's okay for you
to use them) • a pair of scissors • a blank exercise book • a pen
• strong, all-purpose adhesive • roughly 1 m of wide ribbon.

What you do:

1. First cut the legs off the jeans, so that you have two tubes of fabric. Then cut along the inside seams of one of the legs, so that you have a piece of denim with a seam down the centre.

2. Lay the denim flat on a table with the wrong side facing up. Open out the book on top of the piece of fabric, so that the seam runs horizontally across the middle of the cover. Use the pen to draw around it.

3. Draw another rectangle about 3 cm larger around the one you've just drawn, then cut along this outside line.

4. Cover the front of the book with glue, then stick the fabric to it, matching up the edges of the book with the inner rectangle drawn on the fabric. Repeat for the back cover.

5. Cut a diagonal line across the corners, and in the middle at the top and bottom of the fabric, as shown below.

6. Spread a thin line of glue around the three outer edges of the inside front cover of the book. Then fold the edges of the fabric in and stick them down.

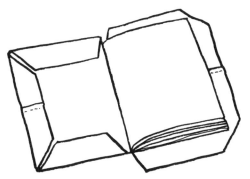

Repeat for the back cover.

7. Cut your length of ribbon in half and add a dab of glue to the end of one piece. Stick it to the inside edge of the front cover. Repeat for the back cover and leave to dry.

Top tip. If your length of ribbon has a wrong side and a right side, glue the right side to the inside covers, so that it shows when you close your note book.

8. Cut carefully around one of the back pockets of your jeans. You should now have a denim pocket with two layers of fabric. Cover the back of the pocket with glue, then stick it to the front of your notebook. Leave to dry.

In-jean-ious!

Decorate her coat and boots.

RODEO ROUNDUP

Come on cowgirls! It's time to complete these challenges to win your very own indoor rodeo. You'll find the answers on page 191.

ROUND 'EM UP!

Which animal has each of these cowgirls lassoed?

Sarah-Jane   Jessie   Lucie   Emmie   Katie

MOST WANTED

One of the cowgirls is on the run from the sheriff – can you spot which one?

WANTED
FOR MAKING
FUN
OF THE SHERIFF

R E W A R D
$500

Goat
Calf   Bull   Pony   Prairie Dog

Who's guilty? . . . .

LASSOSUDOKU

Complete the grid so that each row, each column and each block of four squares contains a boot, a hat, a horseshoe and a sheriff's badge.

WAGON BULL RUN

Run! Get away from the bull to the safety of the wagon. Can you find a route through the Wild West town that passes over just one cactus, one barrel and one tumbleweed?

Key: Cactus   Barrel   Tumbleweed

MIND GAMES

These fun games trick the brain and the body.

SAY WHEN

Ask a friend to hold out her arm and close her eyes. Start stroking the inside of her arm just above her wrist, moving up, down and sideways, but gradually heading towards the inside of her elbow. Tell her to shout when she thinks your finger is directly on the dip at the inside of her elbow. You'd be surprised how many people get this wrong.

BILLY GOAT GRUFF

Ask a friend to stand or sit with her back to you. Say 'How many horns does the billy goat have?' At the same time, press some of the fingers of one hand into her back – spread them as widely as you can. Your friend has to guess how many fingers you are using. The best thing about this game is that young people tend to be better at guessing than adults.

THROUGH THE FLOOR

Ask a friend to lie on her back on the floor. Grab her ankles, and lift her feet off the floor until they're level with your waist.

Ask her to shut her eyes and breathe deeply. Hold her legs in this position for one minute, then very slowly lower them towards the ground. Your friend will expect her legs to reach the floor long before they actually do. She will feel as if her legs are passing through the floor!

MAJOR MIX-UP

The pieces of this jigsaw have got mixed up with some pieces from another jigsaw. Can you work out which three pieces fit in the gaps? The answers are on page 191.

A

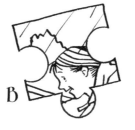

B

C

D

E

F

WHICH SUMMER GODDESS ARE YOU?

Follow this funky flowchart to find out.

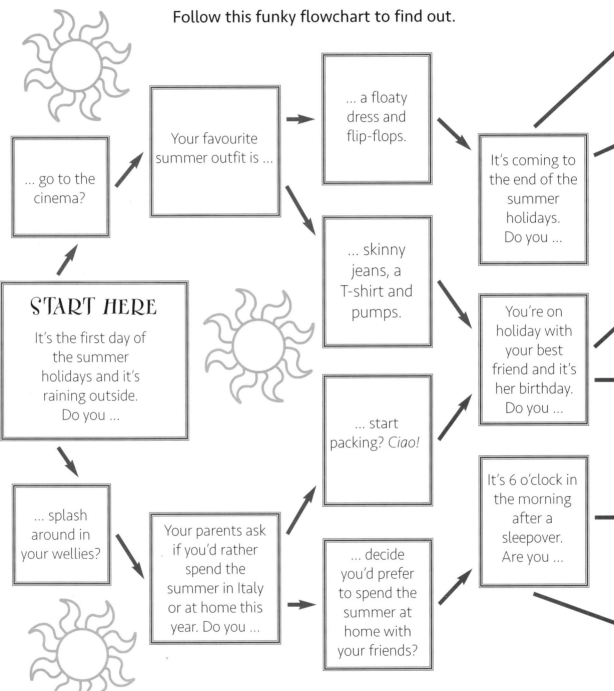

... go to the cinema?

Your favourite summer outfit is ...

... a floaty dress and flip-flops.

It's coming to the end of the summer holidays. Do you ...

START HERE

It's the first day of the summer holidays and it's raining outside. Do you ...

... skinny jeans, a T-shirt and pumps.

You're on holiday with your best friend and it's her birthday. Do you ...

... splash around in your wellies?

... start packing? *Ciao!*

Your parents ask if you'd rather spend the summer in Italy or at home this year. Do you ...

... decide you'd prefer to spend the summer at home with your friends?

It's 6 o'clock in the morning after a sleepover. Are you ...

... make the most of relaxing in your back garden?

... try to pack in as many fun activities as possible?

... plan to go to a theme park she's been talking about?

... invite all the holiday-makers over for a fancy-dress party?

... already getting ready for a fun-filled day?

... tired because you stayed up talking most of the night before?

YOU ARE HEMERA, GODDESS OF SUNSHINE

You love the long summer days and adore playing outside in the sunshine. Complete your goddess look with a sun-shaped hair clip and a yellow ribbon.

YOU ARE AESTAS, GODDESS OF SUMMER

You're bursting with energy. Your friends love that you're full of exciting ideas of things to do and places to visit. Complete your goddess look by pinning plaits of grass into your hair.

YOU ARE IRIS, GODDESS OF RAINBOWS

You love to travel and the summer holidays give you the chance to visit new places and meet new people. Make a necklace of rainbow-coloured beads to complete your goddess look.

YOU ARE ANTHEIA, GODDESS OF FLOWERS

You are a chilled-out girl who likes spending time at home with your friends over the summer holidays. You appreciate the beauty of summer. Pin some fresh flowers in your hair to complete your goddess look.

TREASURE ISLAND

Ahoy there! Head to the treasure island for some puzzle and doodle fun.

A girl is on an island with her mean brother and greedy sister, and a sack of sweets. She needs to get herself, her brother and her sister back to the mainland with the sweets. The raft she has is only large enough to carry her and one thing she needs to take with her, so she will need to make several trips.

The problem is, she can't leave her brother alone with her sister, as he will tease her. She can't leave her sister alone with the sweets, as she will eat them all. Her brother will not eat the sweets, so he can be left alone with them.

Can you work out what she can do? The answer on page 191.

What would you take to a desert island?

BEACH SUDOKU

Complete the grid so that each column, each row, and each of the four larger squares contains only one bucket, a spade, a sand castle and an ice cream.

The answer is on page 192.

Fill the chest with treasure.

CLOSET SWAP SHOP

If you're bored of your clothes and have a wardrobe full of items that you don't wear anymore, why not host a Closet Swap Shop? Follow the steps below and see what new sassy style you end up with.

1. Choose a date for your Closet Swap Shop party and invite your friends around to your house.

2. Ask each friend to bring any clothes, shoes or accessories that they don't wear anymore, and would be happy to swap for something new.

3. On the day of the Swap Shop, designate areas of a room for different items – these might include skirts, tops, dresses, hats, belts, scarves etc.

4. Cut out a differently coloured square of paper for each of the designated areas. Stick a coloured square to the floor, table or chair, next to each area that you have designated.

5. As your guests arrive, ask them to place their items of clothing in the correct areas.

6. Write the name of each guest on to a differently coloured square of paper – according to which item of clothing that they brought to the party. For example, if skirts are in the red area, write the guest's name that brought a skirt on a red square.

7. Put all of the squares with names on into a large bowl and mix them up. Take it in turns to pull a ticket out of the bowl. The guest named on the ticket can then choose an item of clothing from the appropriately coloured pile.

PLAY THE 'STEAL THAT STYLE' GAME

Read on for a different swapping game called 'Steal That Style'. This is a fun game to play at a Closet Swap Shop – the aim is to decide who gets to keep what.

1. Put all the clothes in the middle of the floor.

2. Each player must then choose one of the styles listed below, or think of one of their own.

Boho-Chic   High-street Cool   Sari Sensation

Beach Babe   Sophisticated Sister   Emo

3. Two players then have one minute to look through all the clothes and accessories on display and put together an outfit in the chosen style.

4. The two players then model their outfits. Why not clear a catwalk down the centre of the room for them to walk down like models?

5. The other players then vote for which of the models has done the best job of recreating the style. The model who wins gets to keep one item from their outfit.

6. Repeat with other players and other styles. Happy swapping!

TRAVEL TRIVIA

Test out your family's holiday knowledge with this fun quiz. Use the scorecard opposite to fill in your answers, check to see if they're right on page 192, and find out who is top at travel trivia.

---

1. In which city would you find the River Seine?

A. Madrid

B. Berlin

C. Paris

D. New York

---

2. What is special about Italy's tower of Pisa?

A. It's the tallest tower in the world

B. It's leaning over

C. There is a pizza restaurant at the top

D. You can see it from space

---

3. Which of the following names are you not allowed to call a pig in France.

A. Bill

B. Napoleon

C. Simon

D. Vince

---

4. In which country would you find the deadly funnel-web spider?

A. Iceland

B. France

C. Australia

D. United Kingdom

---

5. What would happen if you jumped into Israel's Dead Sea?

A. You'd freeze

B. You'd sink

C. You'd float

D. You'd be surrounded by sharks

---

6. What is the basic unit of currency in China?

A. Yuan

B. Yan

C. Yen

D. Yin

---

7. In Chile, it is rude to show someone an open palm with the fingers separated. It means you think they are ...

A. Ugly

B. Greedy

C. Lazy

D. Stupid

---

8. Which of the following isn't one of the Seven Wonders of the Ancient World?

A. The Great Pyramids

B. The Hanging Baskets of Babylon

C. The Temple of Achilles

D. The Statue of Zeus at Olympia

9. What are Niagara Falls?

A. Waterfalls

B. Mountains

C. Pyramids

D. Oceans

10. Which of these is a beach in Sydney, Australia?

A. Bondi beach

B. Mouldy beach

C. Fungi beach

D. Tripod beach

11. In which continent is the Amazon Rainforest?

A. Asia

B. Africa

C. South America

D. Europe

12. In which continent is the South Pole found?

A. Europe

B. Antarctica

C. Africa

D. North America

Question	Player 1	Player 2	Player 3	Player 4
1				
2				
3				
4				
5				
6				
7				
8				
9				
10				
11				
12				
Total				

MARVELLOUS MAGIC

Add a bit of magic to your day with these brilliant tricks.

HOW TO SAW A LADY IN HALF

Fool your friends into thinking you are cutting a lady in half ... luckily she is made of paper so, if anything does go wrong, no one gets hurt!

You will need:

• paper • pen • envelope • scissors.

1. To prepare this trick, first seal the envelope shut then cut off the ends to create a tube shape.

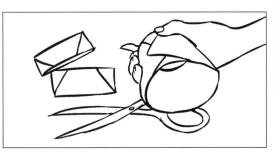

2. Flatten out the tube again, so that the top and bottom of the envelope meet in the middle. Cut two slits from the new edge up to just before the central crease. The slits should separate the tube into thirds.

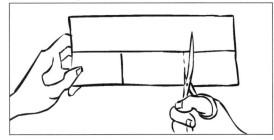

3. Cut a strip of paper, roughly 10 cm wide and about 5 cm longer than the length of your flattened tube shape.

4. Draw a picture of a lady on to the piece of paper, like this:

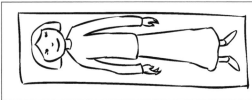

5. Re-shape the flattened tube so that it forms a tube shape again. Position it in the palm of your hand so that the slits are at the back.

6. Slide the paper lady (picture side facing upwards) inside the tube shape, pushing her feet through the first slit so that they come out of the back of the envelope, and then bring her feet back inside the tube by pushing them through the second slit. The back of the tube shape should now look like this:

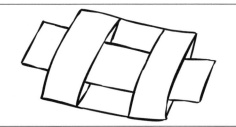

7. To perform the trick, cut the tube in half, making sure that your scissors cut through the middle of the tube – being careful to cut above the paper lady.

8. Finally, pull the lady out from the two pieces of envelope, and amaze your audience when she appears unharmed!

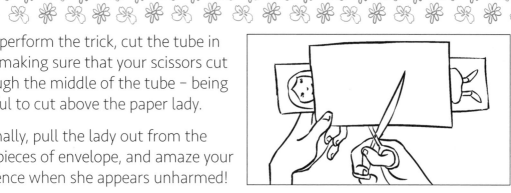

HOW TO CHANGE A BALLOON'S COLOUR

Learn how to make a balloon magically change colour … just by popping it!

You will need:

• a green balloon • a yellow balloon • sticky tape • a pencil • a pin.

1. Before performing this trick, you will need to first make a double-sided loop of sticky tape. Stick it on to the middle of the yellow balloon.

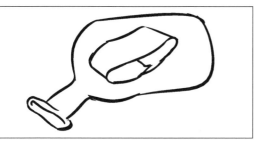

2. Push the unsharpened end of a pencil into the yellow balloon's neck. Then, push the same end into the green balloon. Slide it down until it is completely inside the green balloon.

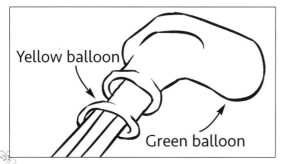

Yellow balloon

Green balloon

3. Blow up the yellow balloon (which will also blow up the green balloon outside it) and tie a knot in the bottom of both balloon necks.

4. Now stand in front of your audience, holding what they will think is a blown up green balloon.

5. Locate where the sticky tape is on the yellow balloon by looking through the green balloon on the outside. Jab a pin in here.

The green balloon will burst, revealing the yellow balloon inside it. It will look like the balloon has magically changed colour!

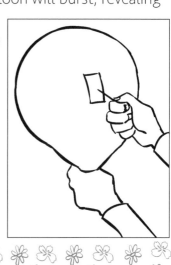

PARTY PUZZLERS

It's party time! Complete these puzzles, then turn to page 192 to check your answers.

VIP PARTY CODE

This party is so top secret that even the invitation has been written in code.

Move each letter two letters backwards in the alphabet to work out where the party is and what time it starts.

For example, if the letter 'c' appears on the invitation, replace it with an 'a'.

Eqog vq Qcm Jqwug qp
Ceqtp Tqcf cv jcnh
rcuv gkijv.

LET'S DANCE

A. How many girls have at least one arm in the air?

B. How many are wearing belts?

C. How many have stars somewhere on their outfits?

D. How many are wearing ballet pumps?

PHOTO FRENZY

Can you work out which parent took each of the photos below?

You need to think about where each one is standing, and which girl they are aiming their camera at. You'll find the answers on page 192.

A MARIE-LOUISE MYSTERY

'The Marie-Louise is one of the world's great maritime mysteries,' Katie read to her brother Jack as they stepped on board the museum ship.

The ship was found abandoned in the Atlantic Ocean in 1864. It looked as though the crew had left suddenly, but there was no obvious reason why the crew would have left. The lifeboats hadn't been used, and there was no sign of a struggle. The Marie-Louise had been carrying a cargo of gold, and none of it was missing.

'Maybe they were kidnapped by pirates?' suggested Jack.

'It can't be pirates,' Katie replied. 'Pirates would've taken the gold.'

'Aliens then! Or a slimy sea monster!'

'There must be a good reason,' declared Katie. 'I'm going to explore below deck.' She headed down the rickety wooden stairs into the dark, damp coolness below and pushed open the door to a small cabin.

Inside, things were exactly as they had been when the ship was found without its crew in 1864. There was a small bed, a wardrobe full of beautiful dresses for a girl of around Katie's age, and a dressing table. *This must be where the captain's daughter slept*, Katie thought.

On the dressing table was a pretty coral comb. Katie knew this was a museum and that she shouldn't touch anything, but she couldn't resist and picked it up.

The comb felt cold and heavy in Katie's hand. She looked at herself in the mirror, just as the captain's daughter must have done all those years ago, and started to comb her hair. As the comb ran through the strands of her hair, Katie could hear music and singing from a long way away. As she continued to comb, it became louder and louder.

The room began to take on a greenish tinge, then vanished altogether. Katie found herself in another room entirely. When she heard a girl's voice chattering behind her, she spun around in surprise.

'A visitor! From above! Welcome, welcome – I'm Amelia. Did you use the comb? I suppose you must have done. No need to look so shocked. Although I was the same when it happened to me. Isn't it fantastic?'

Katie could hardly concentrate on what the excited girl was saying – for instead of legs, Amelia had ... a tail!

'Excuse me,' Katie said, 'but ... are you a mermaid?' She was half-alarmed and half-thrilled.

'Of course,' said Amelia. 'And so are you – look.' She pointed down to where Katie's legs had been, to show her that she had become a mermaid, too!

'You've come to the most wonderful place – and your timing couldn't be better. We're having a party tonight to celebrate my brother's birthday.'

Amelia led her new friend through an underwater palace, stopping in every room to arrange displays of sea-flowers and shining shells. Katie tried to stop and admire the lovely coral walls of the palace, and all the pretty fish darting among them, but she had to swim fast to keep up.

As Amelia talked, Katie discovered that she was the daughter of the Marie-Louise's captain, and that it was because of her that the crew had abandoned the ship all those years ago. Amelia had found the comb hidden beneath the floorboards in her cabin. Her father had watched aghast as she had combed her hair with it and vanished. He had then instructed his entire crew to do the same, so that they could follow her and bring her back to safety.

When the crew discovered the land under the ocean, they loved it so much that none of them wanted to leave. Underwater, they would live for hundreds of years, and as the time

passed, they forgot all about their lives above the ocean and their cargo of gold.

Finally, Amelia stopped talking and declared that it was time to get ready for the party. 'You need some jewels to match those beautiful blues and greens on your tail.' Katie smiled in delight as Amelia handed her a necklace of pearls and wove shells into her hair.

'It's all so magical!' Katie said to Amelia. 'But I can't stay. I left my brother behind, and my parents will be worried.'

Amelia sighed sadly. 'If you leave, you must always protect our secret,' she warned. Katie nodded, and a reluctant Amelia prised open a shell to release a second coral comb. She waved slowly as Katie combed her hair and vanished before her, returning to the ship.

The cabin door swung open and Jack poked his head around it. 'Have you solved the mystery yet?'

Katie quickly removed a piece of seaweed from her hair before her brother could see it. 'Not yet,' she said, as she took his arm and steered him out of the cabin.

SECRET SAFARI

You're visiting a safari park, but where are all the animals?

Below is a map of the safari park. To read it you will need to use coordinates. A coordinate is a letter and a number that refers to a location on a map. To use a coordinate, place your finger on the letter on the left-hand side of the map. Trace your finger along the row to the column that matches the number. In that square you will find the animal that the coordinate refers to.

Can you work out which animals live at the following coordinates?
Check your answers on page 192.

1. D3 **2.** B1 **3.** F3 **4.** C6 **5.** A4 **6.** E6

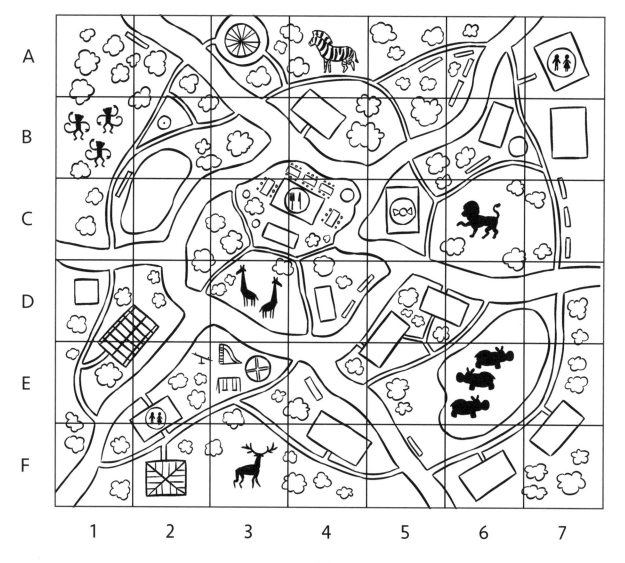

Customize our boards.

SURFER GIRLS

A. How many girls have bikinis?

B. How many have wetsuits?

C. How many have only one foot on their board?

D. How many have ponytails?

Check your answers on page 192.

HEADSCARF HEAVEN

Rainy weather can play havoc with your hairdo, so wrap up in a headscarf to keep your locks looking perfect!

CLASSIC WRAP

1. Take a large square headscarf and fold it in half along the diagonal to create a triangle.

2. Place it over your head so that the middle of the folded side is in the centre of your forehead and the tip is pointing down your back.

3. Take the two ends and tie them in a knot at the back of your head under your hair.

4. Push the front of the headscarf back above your hairline for a softer look.

GYPSY CHIC

1. Hold a sarong over your head so that the middle of one of the long sides is flat against your forehead.

2. Gather the sarong at the nape of your neck, then twist it around all the way to the bottom.

3. Tie a knot in the sarong at the nape of your neck, then pull the length of it forward over your shoulder.

4. Accessorize with some large hoop earrings to complete the gypsy look.

ARABIAN DREAM

1. Tip your head forward and hold a sarong over your head so that the middle of one of the long sides is flat against the nape of your neck.

2. Gather the fabric at your forehead and twist it all the way to the bottom.

3. Lift your head up and take the twisted fabric back over your head and around one side. Then pull it forward over the opposite shoulder.

4. Accessorize with lots of sparkly bangles.

VINTAGE QUEEN

1. Take a square headscarf and fold it in half to create a triangle.

2. Hold the headscarf across your shoulders so that the tip is pointing down your back and the straight edge is underneath your hair.

3. Pick up the two ends and tie them in a knot on top of your head.

4. Pull the point of the scarf up over your head, tucking long hair away inside, then slip the end of the scarf under the front of the knot.

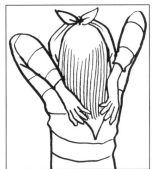

5. Tie the ends in a second knot to ensure the point stays in place, then tuck the ends in too.

6. Wear with a stripy sailor top to complete the look.

Fill the page with snowflakes.

ROLLER-SKATE RACE

These identical twins are having a roller-skating race. Can you spot ten differences between them? Check your answers on page 192.

Draw more trees in the park.

HIT THE SLOPES

Race for the finish line with this snowy ski game.

Place a coin for each player by the START line.
Then ski down the mountain, keeping an
eye out for sneaky shortcuts, or traps
that could slow you down.
The first one to the FINISH
is the winner.

START

A bear is
chasing you. R
again to get av

You spot an off-piste
shortcut.
Jump ahead.

There's a
blizzard.
Miss a turn while
you wait for it
to pass.

You hitch a ride
on a sledge.
Take the shortcut.

You crash into
another skier.
Move back
2 spaces.

You learn a new trick.
Roll a 6 to master it
and win.

FINISH

SPINNER

CUT OUT

Cut out this spinner.
Stick a toothpick
through the middle
of it.

You fly over a
ski jump.
Move forward
2 spaces.

You stop for a drink
at a ski café.
Miss a turn.

You twist
your ankle.
Miss a turn.

You skid on
some ice.
Move forward
2 spaces.

IN A SPIN

To spin your spinner, hold the toothpick upright with one
hand, and spin the spinner with the other. The number that
is at the top of the spinner when it stops tells you the
number of spaces you should move.

179

TREASURE HUNT

Next time you go away, look out for the following items and stick them in when you find them.

Try to find everything before it's time for you to go home.

1. A picture of somewhere you visited cut out from a brochure or leaflet.

2. A section of a map that shows where you are staying.

3. A ticket from a journey you went on.

4. A stamp from the country you're in.

5. A napkin from a café or restaurant.

6. A price tag or sticker.

7. The wrapper of a sweet you've never tried before.

8. The smallest coin available in the country you're in.

TOP THAT!

Make a set of personalized *Top That!* cards to play with your friends or to give to someone as a special gift.

You will need:

• 2 pieces of thin A4 card • scissors
• old magazines with lots of photos of celebrities • a glue stick • a black pen
• transparent sticky-back plastic (optional).

1. Fold each piece of card into thirds across the width, then cut along the lines to get six short strips of card.

2. Fold each strip of card into thirds to make playing-card sized rectangles. Cut along the folds so that you have 18 small cards.

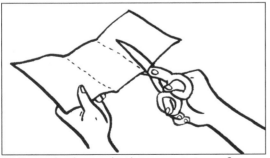

3. Search through the magazines for photos of actors and singers that you like. Look for pictures where the heads are roughly 3 cm high. You'll need pictures of 18 different people altogether.

4. When you have chosen your magazine pictures, cut around each person's head. Glue each of the heads at the top of a card, leaving space underneath to write.

Dress sense: · · · · · · · · ·
Singing skills: · · · · · · · ·
Acting ability: · · · · · · · ·
Hair style: · · · · · · · · · · ·
Kindness to fans: · · · · · ·

5. Now choose five categories to rate each celebrity on. For example, you might pick: dress sense, singing skills, acting ability, hair style and kindness to fans – or pick your own categories.

Score each person out of 10 in each of the categories to complete the cards.

Top Tip. Make sure that you include at least one high score and at least one low score on each card.

6. For a long-lasting finish, cover your cards in transparent sticky-back plastic.

HOW TO PLAY

Any number of people can play *Top That!* Deal the cards face down. Each player then takes their top card and the player to the left of the dealer reads out one of their categories and the score, for example:

'Singing skills: 8.'

The other players then read out the same category, and the player with the highest value wins all the cards from that round. That player then puts the card to the bottom of her pile, and picks a category to play from the card on the top.

If two or more players share the top score for a category, all the cards from that round are placed in the middle and the same player chooses another category from her next card. The winner of the round wins all the cards from the middle as well as the cards in play.

The player with all the cards at the end is the winner.

SPOT THAT DIFFERENCE!

There are five differences between the two pictures of the girl playing Top That! Can you spot them all? You'll find the answers on page 192.

ALL THE ANSWERS

FREAKY FOOD
page 11

The following foods are eaten in the following countries:

Maggoty cheese in Italy; snake blood in Vietnam; tequila worms in Mexico; snails in France; digested coffee in Sumatra; rats in North Korea; spiders in Cambodia; jellied eels in the United Kingdom; bird spit in China; grasshoppers in Africa.

SHOP 'TIL YOU DROP
pages 12 and 13

In the sweet shop you could buy:
17 cola bottles with 11p left over,
6 bonbons, 30 humbugs, 15 toffees,
9 lollipops with 3p left over,
5 liquorices, 3 candy canes with 45p left over, 12 sugar mice,
6 sherbet lemons with 30p left over.

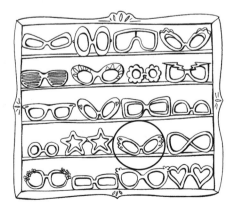

CRACK THOSE CODES
page 17

Bottle 1 use clue 2:
Riddle: 'I have arms, legs and a back, but I never walk anywhere.
What am I?'
Answer: I am a chair.

Bottle 2 use clue 3:
Riddle: 'Say it and you will break it.
What is it?'
Answer: Silence.

Bottle 3 use clue 1:
Riddle: 'The more you take of these the more you leave behind.
What are they?'
Answer: Footsteps.

PICNIC PUZZLE
page 19

☐ 11 Strawberries
○ 6 Cupcakes

AMAZING ANIMAL FACTS
page 23

The false fact is number **6**. Elephant pregnancies are in fact on average 22 months long – more than twice as long as human pregnancies!

PUZZLE HOTEL
pages 36 and 37

Room keys **C** and **L** are identical.

KITE CONFUSION
page 20

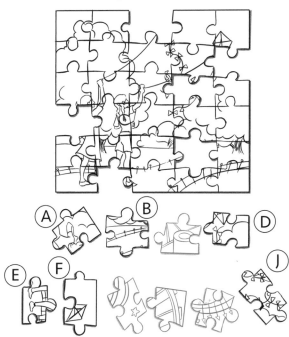

Person **1** has bag **A**.
Person **2** has bag **C**.
Person **3** has bag **D**.
Person **4** has bag **B**.

GARDEN GAMES
page 41

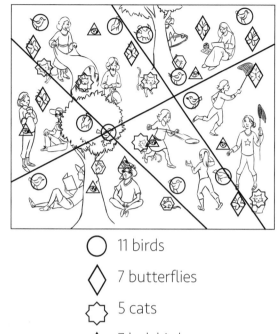

○ 11 birds

◇ 7 butterflies

✦ 5 cats

△ 7 ladybirds

⬡ 3 mice

PURR-FECT PETS
page 51

○ 4 dogs
✦ 3 rabbits
△ 4 cats
◇ 1 bird
☆ 5 hamsters
⬡ 3 fish
♡ 1 snake

HOME SWEET HOME
pages 66 and 67

Girl **1** has bed **B**.
Girl **2** has bed **C**.
Girl **3** has bed **A**.
Girl **4** has bed **D**.

HELLO, HANJIE!
page 70

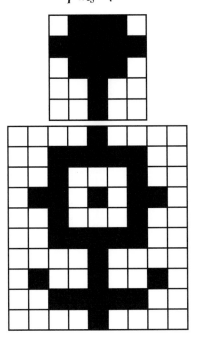

Dressing-Gown Dilemma
Dressing gown **C** belongs to Jenny.
Dressing gown **D** belongs to Jo.
Dressing gown **A** belongs to Kim.
Dressing gown **B** belongs to Katie.

Snack Time!
C and **D** are the matching pizza slices.

Middle-Name Logic
Jo's middle name is Isabelle.
Katie's middle name is Coral.
Kim's middle name is Sophie.
Jenny's middle name is Sarah.

TREASURE HUNT
page 87

The treasure is in the ice-cream stall.

SLEEPOVER PUZZLER
pages 80 and 81

SLEEPOVER MYSTERY MAZE

AT THE SEASIDE
pages 92 and 93

Squares **A**, **D**, **F** and **H**.

A. Six, **B.** Five,
C. Seven, **D.** Zero.

SUPER SNAPS
page 99

1. E, **2.** D, **3.** A,
4. B, **5.** F, **6.** C.

MAP MAYHEM
page 100

5A is a swimming pool.
4E is a café.
1F is a school.
3B is a theme park.
6D is a hospital.
3G is a cinema.

BAGS OF DIFFERENCE
page 103

B

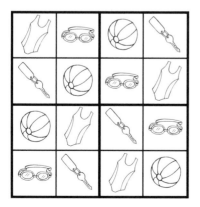

WATER WORLD
pages 108 and 109

Swimmer A reaches flume 1.
Swimmer B reaches flume 2.
Swimmer C reaches flume 3.
Swimmer D reaches flume 4.

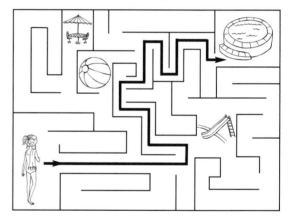

FASHIONISTA FUN
page 118

The matching girls are E and H.

DANCE AROUND
THE WORLD
page 119

A is Spain.
B is France.
C is India.
D is Egypt.

E is China.
F is Ghana.
G is Brazil.
H is USA.

FASHION FRENZY
page 120

Model **A** has dog **5**.
Model **B** has dog **4**.
Model **C** has dog **2**.
Model **D** has dog **1**.
Model **E** has dog **3**.

Model **C** doesn't have a matching pair.

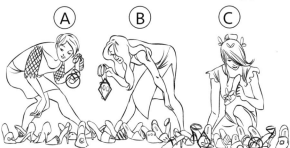

HAWAIIAN LUAU
pages 130 and 131

The party is at the Halona Blowhole.

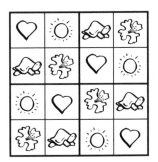

Smoothie **A** is yours.

THEATRELAND
pages 126 and 127

Photo **A** was taken by photographer **6**.
Photo **B** was taken by photographer **3**.
Photo **C** was taken by photographer **4**.
Photo **D** was taken by photographer **1**.
Photo **E** was taken by photographer **5**.
Photo **F** was taken by photographer **2**.

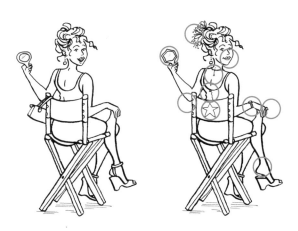

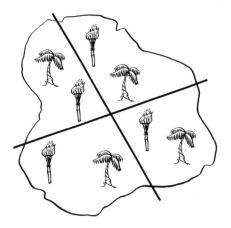

GET YOUR SKATES ON
page 136

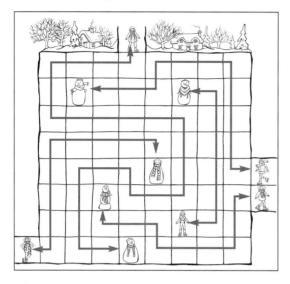

BRAIN-BASHERS
pages 138 and 139

Trophy Time
Alex has three trophies. Here's why: If Alex had won 'at least five' trophies, then Alyssa and Emily would both be right as that is 'more than one'. If he had won an even number of trophies, as Preeya says, Emily would also be right as that is always more than one. Emily's is the only answer that can be right when the other girls' answers are wrong.

Sunflower Sums
Because the sunflower doubles in height every day, and is as tall as her after 30 days, it will be half her height the day before, after 29 days.

Summer Fun
The fourth child is Summer!

Donkey Dilemma

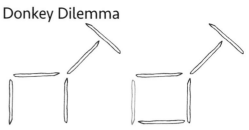

Chocolate Conundrum
If Rebecca removes a chocolate from the box marked 'Milk and White Chocolate', the solution is simple.

All of the labels are wrong, so the box marked 'Milk and White Chocolate' must contain either milk or white chocolate. If Rebecca gets a milk chocolate, then that box must contain only milk chocolates. This means that the box that is marked 'White Chocolate' must be the mixed box and the remaining box should have the 'White Chocolate' label.

Who's the top?
Louisa is 105 cm tall.
Siân 100 cm tall.
Sally 115 cm tall.
Preeya 110 cm tall.

PUPPY POWER
page 147

Puppy **A** belongs to **Rosie**.
Puppy **B** belongs to **Leila**.
Puppy **C** belongs to **Caitlin**.

DID YOU KNOW?
page 149

FACT 4 is wrong. Wearing light colours actually keeps you cool on a sunny day. Dark colours absorb heat, whereas light colours reflect it.

FUN ON THE FARM
pages 150 and 151

17 apples and 12 birds.

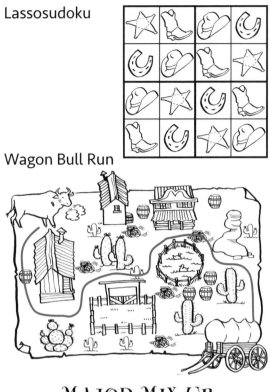

Lassosudoku

Wagon Bull Run

MAJOR MIX-UP
page 157

The missing pieces of the jigsaw puzzle are **B**, **C** and **E**.

TREASURE ISLAND
page 160

The girl takes the sister across to the mainland, leaving the brother and the sweets. She returns to the island, and takes her brother to the mainland. Then she takes her sister back to the island with her – so that her brother and sister aren't left alone together.

Next, she leaves her sister on the island, takes the sweets across to the mainland and leaves them with her brother. Finally, she returns to the island and takes her sister back to the mainland.

RODEO ROUNDUP
pages 154 and 155

Round 'Em Up!
Sarah-Jane has lassoed a bull.
Jessie has lassoed a pony.
Lucie has lassoed a goat.
Emmie has lassoed a calf.
Katie has lassoed a prairie dog.

Most Wanted
Sarah-Jane is on the run.

BEACH SUDOKU
page 161

TRAVEL TRIVIA
pages 164 and 165

1. C, 2. B, 3. B, 4. C,
5. C, 6. A, 7. D, 8. B,
9. A, 10. A, 11. C, 12. B.

PARTY PUZZLERS
page 168

The coded party invitation says:
Come to Oak House on Acorn Road at half past eight.

A. Five girls have at least one arm in the air.
B. Three girls are wearing belts.
C. Five girls have stars on their outfits.
D. Three girls are wearing ballet pumps.

PHOTO FRENZY
page 169

A. 2, B. 4, C. 5,
D. 1, E. 3, F. 6.

SECRET SAFARI
page 172

1. Giraffes
2. Monkeys
3. Deer
4. Lion
5. Zebra
6. Hippos

SURFER GIRLS
page 173

A. five, B. seven, C. two, D. seven.

ROLLER-SKATE RACE
page 177

SPOT THAT DIFFERENCE!
page 183

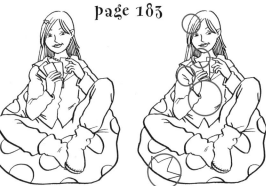